OSI Standards and Acronyms

Third Edition

Compiled by Dr Adrian V Stokes

British Library Cataloguing in Publication Data

OSI Standards and Acronyms - - 3rd ed.

   1. Computer systems. Communication networks
   International standards. Open Systems
   Interconnection - Encyclopaedias
   I. Stokes, Adrian V.

ISBN

© Adrian V Stokes 1991

Printed in the UK

PREFACE

One of the fastest expanding fields in computing is that of telecommunications and, in particular, *"Open Systems Interconnection"* (OSI).

Work started on OSI in 1977 and its aim was to allow the interconnection of equipment from different manufacturers by specifying appropriate standards in this area. Since the publication of the *"ISO Reference Model of Open Systems Interconnection"* in 1983, there has been a plethora of standards conforming to this Model. Most major manufacturers have committed themselves to OSI and many products are available.

In this field (as with many other rapidly changing fields), it is often difficult to get precise information, such as titles of standards, although these are in the public domain. Similarly, the field is awash with acronyms and abbreviations, the majority of which are unlikely to be in dictionaries of computing (either because they are too specialised or too recent).

This publication attempts to overcome these problems. In a single publication, it lists the major national and international standards in this field, together with a list of relevant acronyms and abbreviations. Although intended principally to cover OSI, this is deliberately interpreted widely and it has been decided to err on the side of giving too much information rather than too little. In some cases, it may not be clear why a standard is included (for example, the ISO standard on metric screw thread sizes; in this case, it is referred to by standards in the Physical Layer of the Model).

As stated above, the information contained in this book is all in the public domain and this is merely a collation of such information. As this is a rapidly moving field, the information will become out of date and so the first Chapter not only gives a brief indication of the relevant standards-making bodies but also gives their addresses so that, if necessary, up-to-date information may be obtained.

This third edition, is more than twice the size of its predecessor, demonstrating the rapid increase in the number of standards over the last two years. A major change is the inclusion of European standards, from CEN/CENELEC and ETSI. Such a book as this cannot claim to be fully comprehensive but it is hoped that the majority of OSI standards up to mid-1991 are included.

It also includes a new section containing some brief information on the standards bodies and the manner in which they operate.

Adrian V.Stokes   June 1991

CONTENTS

PART I

STANDARDS MAKING BODIES

1   HISTORY AND BACKGROUND

There are two major international standards-making bodies, ISO (the International Standards Organisation) and CCITT (the Comité Consultatif International Télégraphique et Téléphonique). In broad terms, ISO is responsible for data processing standards whereas CCITT is responsible for "Recommendations" in the field of public telecommunications services. However, there is considerable overlap and the two organisations have a number of standards in common.

1.1   CCITT

CCITT is one of the four "permanent bodies" of the International Telecommunications Union (ITU). It was formed in 1956 by a merger between two organisations set up in 1925 by ITU, the CCIF (the Comité Consultatif International des Communications Téléphoniques à Grande Distance) and the corresponding telegraph body, CCIT. ITU is itself a specialised agency of the United Nations (as is, for example, the World Health Organisation).

CCITT's members are the telecommunications authorities (PTTs) in the various countries in the world.

1.2   ISO

ISO was formed in 1947 and consists of various organisations, especially the national standards bodies (such as the British Standards Institution (BSI) and the American National Standards Institute (ANSI)). In addition, other organisations (such as CCITT) have observer status. There is close co-operation between ISO and CCITT.

Standards are voted into existence by ISO, following extensive consultation and a vote of 75% in favour is required.

1.3   IEC

The International Electrotechnical Commission was founded in 1906 by, amongst others, Lord Kelvin and Charles Steinmetz. It is also concerned with the creation of international standards, especially concerned with electrical safety.

Of particular interest is that, a few years ago, the IEC and ISO TC97 formed "Joint Technical Committee One" (JTC1) and many OSI standards are produced under the auspices of this committee.

1.4   European Standards Bodies

There are two major international standards bodies for Europe, CEN (founded in 1961) and CENELEC (1973), the latter being concerned with electrotechnical standardisation while the former has a more general remit (cf. ISO and IEC). As with ISO, the member bodies of CEN/CENELEC are the national standards bodies but there is one significant difference, namely that European Standards from CEN/CENELEC (known as "European Norms" (ENs)) are mandatory on all participating countries. There are eighteen such countries, including the EC and EFTA countries. When voting formally, each country has a weighted vote. Table 1 shows the members of CEN/CENELEC and their voting weights.

Country	Weight	Country	Weight
Austria	3	Italy	10
Belgium	5	Luxembourg	2
Denmark	3	Netherlands	5
Finland	3	Norway	3
France	10	Portugal	5
Germany	10	Spain	8
Greece	5	Sweden	5
Iceland	1	Switzerland	5
Ireland	3	UK	10

Table 1: CEN Members and Voting Weights

1.5   Other Standards Bodies

There is a wide range of other bodies which produce standards, varying in their importance and power. Since their standards are listed later in this book, it is worth mentioning the (US) Electronic Industries Association (perhaps best known for its "Recommended Standard" RS-232) and the Institute of Electrical and Electronics Engineers, a US professional body which produces standards, usually under the auspices of ANSI.

In addition to these bodies, there are innumerable others, such as consortia of manufacturers.

2 ORGANIZATION AND WORK AREAS

2.1 CCITT

CCITT operates in Study Periods of four years each and, at the end of the Study Period, it produces standards (formally known as *"Recommendations"*). The work is carried out by a number of "Study Groups" and a list of current Study Groups is given in Table 2. The Recommendations approved at the end of each Study Period are published in a form known by the colour of the cover. Thus the 1984 Recommendations are known as the "Red Book", the 1988 ones as the "Blue Book" and the 1992 ones will become the "White Book".

Of particular concern are the V-series recommendations (concerned with analogue communications) and the X-series (digital). A list of all series is given in Table 3.

2.2 ISO

ISO uses a hierarchical structure consisting of a number of Technical Committees (e.g. TC97 is concerned with information processing systems), each of which has a number of Sub-Committees.

Standards usually start as a "Working Draft" (WD) in a Sub-Committee, then are registered as a "Committee Draft" (CD) (previously known as a "Draft Proposal" (DP)). After a six-month ballot, the standard can be registered as a "Draft International Standard" (DIS) provided that two-thirds of the P-members (i.e. those who have registered their desire to participate in that particular standardisation work) vote in favour of progression and less than one quarter of all the member bodies voting vote against. It may then proceed to be registered as a full "International Standard" (IS) following a similar procedure.

SG	Title
I	Definition, operation and quality of service aspects of telgraph, data transmission and telematic services
II	Operation of the telephone network and ISDN
III	General tariff principles including accounting
IV	Transmission maintenance of international lines, circuits and chains of circuits; maintenance of automatic and semi-automatic networks
V	Protection against dangers and disturbances of electromagnetic origin
VI	Outside plant
VII	Data communication networks
VIII	Terminal equipment for telematic services
IX	Telegraph networks and terminal equipment
X	Languages and methods for telecommunications applications
XI	ISDN and telephone network signalling and switching
XII	Transmission performance of telephone networks and terminals
XV	Transmission systems
XVII	Data transmission over the telephone network
XVIII	Digital networks including ISDN

Table 2: CCITT Study Groups

Series	Scope
A	Organisation of the work of the CCITT
B	Means of expression (definitions, symbols, classification)
C	General telecommunications statistics
D	General tariff principles
E	International telephone operation, network management and traffic engineering
F	Telegraph, telematic, message handling and directory services; operations, quality of service and definition of service
G	Transmission systems and media, digital systems and networks
H	Line transmission of non-telephone signals
I	Integrated Services Digital Networks (ISDN)
J	Transmission of sound programme and television signals
K	Protection against interference
L	Construction, installation and protection of cable and other elements of outside plant
M	Maintenance: international transmission systems, telephone circuits, telegraphy, facsimile and leased circuits
N	Maintenance: international sound programme and television transmission circuits
O	Specifications of measuring equipment
P	Telephone transmission quality, telephone installations, local line networks
Q	Telephone switching and signalling
R	Telegraph transmission
S	Telegraph services terminal equipment
T	Terminal equipment and protocols for telematic services
U	Telegraph switching
V	Data communication over the telephone network
X	Data communication networks
Z	Programming languages

Table 3: CCITT Series of Recommendations

An international standards is known as "ISO xxxx-n:dddd" where "xxxx" is the number of the standard, "n" is the part number (which may be omitted) and "dddd" is the date (e.g. ISO 7498:1984). Standards developed in JTC1 (see above) have "ISO" replaced by "ISO/IEC".

2.3   CEN/CENELEC

Members of these organisations have weighted votes when voting for standards (e.g. formal approval of ENs, ENVs and HDs) as described above. For a weighted vote to be passed, there are a number of criteria that must be complied with. These are:

- A simple majority of members in favour (unweighted votes)
- At least 25 affirmative weighted votes
- At most 22 negative weighted votes
- At most 3 members voting against.

However, if any of the criteria are not satisfied, the votes of non-EEC countries are excluded and the criteria re-examined.

3   ADDRESSES OF STANDARDS BODIES

3.1   International

CCITT   Place des Nations   Tel: +41 22 730 51 11
              1211 Geneva 20   Fax: +41 22 733 72 56
              SWITZERLAND   Tlx: 421000 UIT CH

ISO   1 rue de Varembe   Tel: +41 22 34 12 40
              Case postale 56   Fax: +41 22 33 34 30
              CH-1211 Geneva 20   Tlx: 23887 ISO CH
              SWITZERLAND

IEEE   345 East 47th Street
              New York
              NY 10017
              USA

3.2   European

CEN   rue de Stassart 36   Tel: +32 2 519 6811
              B-1050 BRUSSELS   Fax: +32 2 519 6819
              Belgium   Tlx: 172210097

CENELEC   rue de Stassart 35   Tel: +32 2 519 6871
              B-1050 BRUSSELS   Fax: +32 2 519 6919
              Belgium   Tlx: 172210097

CEPT   Case Postale 1283   Tel: +41 31 62.20.79
                  CH-3001 BERNE   Fax: 911089 CEPT CH
                  SWITZERLAND

ECMA   rue du Rhone 114   Tel: +41 22 35.36.34
                  CH-1204 GENEVA   Fax: +41 22 86.52.31
                  Switzerland   Tlx: 22288 ECMA CH

ETSI   B.P. 152   Tel: +33 92 94 42 00
                  F-06561 Valbonne Cedex   Fax: +33 93 65 47 16
                  France   Tlx: 470 040 F

EWOS   rue de Stassart 36   Tel: +32 2 511 7455
                  B-1050   Fax: +32 2 511 8723
                  BRUSSELS   Tlx: 26257 CENLEC B
                  Belgium

SPAG   Avenue Louise 149, Box 7   Tel: +32 2 535 08 11
                  B-1050 Brussels   Fax: +32 2 537 24 40
                  Belgium   Tlx: 20307 SPAG B

3.3   National

Austria   Osterreichisches normungsinstitut Tel: +43 1 26 75 35
                  Postfach 130   Fax: +43 1 26 75 52
                  Heinestrasse 38   Tlx: 115960
                  A-1021 WIEN 2
                  AUSTRIA

Belgium   Institute Belge de Normalisation   Tel: +32 2 734 92 05
                  Avenue de la Brabanconne 29   Fax: +32 2 733 42 64
                  B-1040 Bruxelles   Tlx: 23877 BENOR B
                  BELGIUM

Denmark   Dansk Standardiseringsrad   Tel: +45 31 62 32 00
                Postboks 77   Fax: +45 31 62 30 77
                Aurehojvej 12   Tlx: 15615 DANSTA DK
                DK-2900 HELLERUP
                DENMARK

Finland   Suomen Standardisoimisliitto SFS   Tel: +358 0 64 56 01
                PL 205   Fax: +358 0 64 31 47
                Bulevardi 5 A 7   Tlx: 122303 STAND SF
                SF-00121 HELSINKI 12
                FINLAND

France   Association Française de   Tel: +33 1 4291 5555
                     Normalisation   Fax: +33 1 4291 5656
                Tour Europe - Cedex 7   Tlx: AFNOR 611974 F
                92080 Paris La Défense
                FRANCE

Germany   Deutsches Institut für Normung   Tel: +49 30 2601 452
                Burggrafenstrasse 4-10   Fax: +49 30 260 1231
                Postfach 1107   Tlx: 184273 DIN D
                D-1000 Berlin 30
                West Germany

Greece   Ellinikos Organismos Typopolisis   Tel: +30 1 201 50 25
                Achamon St 313   Fax: +30 1 364 45 69
                GR-111 45 ATHENS   Tlx: 219621 ELOT GR
                GREECE

Iceland   Technological Institute of Iceland Tel: +354 1 68 70 00
                     (Standards Division)   Fax: +354 1 68 14 09
                Keldnaholt   Tlx: 3020 ISTECH IS
                112 REYKJAVIK
                ICELAND

Ireland   National Standards Authority of   Tel: +353 1 370101
                 Ireland   Fax: +353 1 379620
                 Ballymun Road   Tlx: 32501 IIRS EI
                 Dublin 9
                 IRELAND

Italy   Ente Nazionale Italiano di   Tel: +39 2 72 00 11 41
                 Unificazione   Fax: +39 2 869 01 20
                 Plazza Armando Diaz 2   Tlx: 312481 UNI I
                 I-20123 MILANO
                 Italy

Luxembourg Inspection du Travail et des Mines   Tel: +352 49 92 21 06
                 Rue Zithe 26   Fax: +352 49 14 47
                 B.P. 26
                 2010 LUXEMBOURG

Netherlands Nederlands Normalisatie-instituut   Tel: +31 15 690 390
                 Postbus 5059   Fax: +31 15 690 190
                 2600 GB Delft   Tlx: 38144 NNI NL
                 HOLLAND

Norway   Norges Standardiseringsforbund   Tel: +47 2 46 60 94
                 Homansbyen   Fax: +47 2 46 44 57
                 Postboks 7020   Tlx: 19050 NSF N
                 N-0306 OSLO 3
                 Norway

Portugal   Instituto Portugues da Qualidade   Tel: +351 1 53 98 91
                 Rua Jose Estevao, 83A   Fax: +351 1 53 00 33
                 1199 LISBOA Codex   Tlx: 13 042 QUALIT P
                 Portugal

Spain   Asociación Española de   Tel: +34 1 410 48 51
                       Normalizatión y Certificación   Fax: +34 1 410 49 76
                   Calle Fernandez de la Hoz 52   Tlx:
                   28010 MADRID

Sweden   Standardiseringskommissinen i   Tel: +46 823 04 00
                       Sverige   Fax: +46 811 70 35
                   Box 3295   Tlx: 17453 SIS S
                   Tegnergatan 11, Box 3 295
                   S-103 66 Stockholm 6
                   SWEDEN

Switzerland   Schweizerische Normen-   Tel: +41 1 47 69 70
                       Vereinigung/Association   Fax: +41 1 47 08 80
                       Suisse de Normalisation   Tlx: 755931 SNV CH
                   Kirchenweg 4 - Postfach
                   8032 Zurich
                   SWITZERLAND

USA   American National Standards   Tel: +1 212 354 3300
                       Institute   Fax: +1 212 302 1286
                   1430 Broadway   Tlx: 424296 ANSI UI
                   New York
                   NY 10018
                   USA

United   British Standards Institution   Tel: +44 71 629 9000
Kingdom   2 Park Street   Fax: +44 71 629 0506
                   LONDON   Tlx: 266933 BSILDN G
                   W1A 2BS
                   UNITED KINGDOM

PART II

LISTS OF STANDARDS

1   INTERNATIONAL STANDARDS

1.1   1984 CCITT Recommendations

A-Series Recommendations

A.1   Presentation of contributions relative to the study of
               questions assigned to the CCITT

A.10   Terms and definitions

A.12   Collaboration with the International Electrotechnical
               Commission on the subject of definitions for tele-
               communications

A.13   Collaboration with the International Electrotechnical
               Commission on graphical symbols and diagrams used
               in telecommunications

A.14   Publication of definitions

A.15   Presentation of CCITT texts

A.16   Presentation of texts on terminology

A.17   Collaboration concerning maintenance considerations
               for new systems

A.21   Collaboration with other international organizations on
               CCITT-defined telematic services

B-Series Recommendations

C-Series Recommendations

E-Series Recommendations

E.163   Numbering plan for the international telephone service

E.164   Numbering plan for the ISDN era

E.171   International telephone routing plan

E.300   Special uses of circuits normally employed for automatic telephone traffic

E.401   Statistics for the international telephone service (number of circuits in operation and volume of traffic)

F-Series Recommendations

F.5   General aspects of Group 4 facsimile apparatus

F.10   Character error rate objective for telegraph communication using 5-unit start-stop equipment

F.51   Coded character sets for telematic services

F.60   Operational provisions for the international Telex service

F.61   Measurement of the chargeable duration of an international Telex call for charging and accounting purposes

F.62   Duplex operation in the Telex service

F.63   Additional facilities in the international Telex service

F.64   Determination of the number of international Telex circuits required to carry a given volume of traffic

F.66   Regional tariff recommendations for the international Telex service

F.67   Charging and accounting in the international Telex service

F.68   Establishment of the automatic intercontinental Telex network

F.350   Application of Series T Recommendations

G-Series Recommendations

G.101   The transmission plan

G.102   Transmission performance objectives and recommendations

G.103   Hypothetical reference connections

G.104   Hypothetical reference connections (digital networks)

G.104   Hypothetical reference connection for crosstalk studies

G.106   Terms and definitions related to quality of service, availability and reliability

G.107   General considerations and model of a basic telephone call

G.108   Models for the allocation of international telephone connection retainability

G.111   Corrected reference equivalents (CREs) and loudness ratings (LRs) in an international connection

G.113   Transmission impairments

G.114   Mean one-way propagation time

G.117   Transmission aspects of unbalance about earth (definitions and methods)

G.120   Transmission characteristics of national networks

G.121   Corrected reference equivalents (CREs) and loudness ratings (LRs) of national systems

G.122   Influence of national systems on stability, talker echo and listener echo in international connections

G.123   Circuit noise in national networks

G.125   Characteristics of national circuits on carrier systems

G.131   Stability and echo

G.132   Attenuation distortion

G.133   Group delay distortion

G.134   Linear crosstalk

G.135   Error on the reconstituted frequency

G.141   Transmission losses, relative levels and attenuation distortion

G.142   Transmission characteristics of exchanges

G.143   Circuit noise and the use of compandors

G.151   General performance objectives applicable to all modern international circuits and national extension circuits

G.152   Characteristics appropriate to long-distance circuits of a length not exceeding 2500 Km

G.153   Characteristics appropriate to international circuits more than 2500 Km in length

G.161   Echo-suppressors suitable for circuits having either short or long propagation times

G.162   Characteristics of compandors for telephony

G.163   Call concentrating systems

G.164   Echo suppressors

G.165   Echo cancellers

G.166   Characteristics of syllabic compandors for telephony on high capacity long distance systems

G.171   Transmission plan aspects of privately operated networks

G.172   Transmission plan aspects of international conference calls

G.180   Connection accessibility objective for the international telephone service

G.181   Connection retainability objective for the international telephone service

G.211   Make-up of a carrier link

G.212   Hypothetical reference circuits for analogue systems

G.213   Interconnection of systems in a main repeater station

G.214   Line stability of cable systems

G.215   Hypothetical reference circuit of 5000 Km for analogue systems

G.221   Overall Recommendations relating to carrier-transmission systems

G.222   Noise objectives for design of carrier-transmission systems of 2500 Km

G.223   Assumptions for the calculation of noise on hypothetical reference circuits for telephony

G.224   Maximum permissible value for the absolute power level (power referred to one milliwatt) of signalling pulse

G.225   Recommendations relating to the accuracy of carrier frequencies

G.226   Noise on a real link

G.227   Conventional telephone signal

G.228   Measurement of circuit noise in cable systems using a uniform-spectrum random noise ioading

G.229   Unwanted modulation and phase jitter

G.332   12-MHz systems on standardized 2.6/9.5 mm coaxial cable pairs

G.333   60 MHz systems on standardized 2.6/9.5 mm coaxial cable pairs

G.334   18 MHz systems on standardized 2.6/9.5 mm coaxial cable pairs

G.337   General characteristics of systems on standardized 2.6/9.5 mm coaxial cable pairs

G.338   4 MHz valve-type systems on standardized 2.6/9.5 mm coaxial cable pairs

G.339   12 MHz valve-type systems on standardized 2.6/9.5 mm coaxial cable pairs

G.341   1.3 MHz systems on standardized 1.2/4.4 mm coaxial cable pairs

G.343   4 MHz systems on standardized 1.2/4.4 mm coaxial cable pairs

G.344   6 MHz systems on standardized 1.2/4.4 mm coaxial cable pairs

G.345   12 MHz systems on standardized 1.2/4.4 mm coaxial cable pairs

G.346   18 MHz systems on standardized 1.2/4.4 mm coaxial cable pairs

G.352   Interconnection of coaxial carrier systems of different designs

G.356   (120 + 120) channel systems on a single coaxial pair

G.361   Systems providing three carrier telephone circuits on a pair of open-wire lines

G.371   FDM carrier systems for submarine cable

G.411   Use of radio relay systems for international telephone circuits

G.471   Conditions necessary for interconnection of mobile radiotelephone stations and international telephone lines

G.473   Interconnection of a maritime mobile satellite system with the international automatic switched telephcne service - transmission aspects

G.541   Specification of factory lengths of loaded tele-communication cable

G.542   Specification of loading coils for loaded tele-communication cables

G.543   Specification for repeater sections of loaded tele-communication cable

G.544   Specification for terminal equipment and intermediate repeater stations

G.601   Terminology for cables

G.602   Reliability and availability of analogue cable transmission systems and associated equipments

G.611   Characteristics of symmetric cable pairs for analogue transmission

G.612   Characteristics of symmetric cable pairs designed for the transmission of systems with bit rates of the order of 6 to 34 Mbit/s

G.613   Characteristics of symmetric cable pairs usable wholly for the transmission of digital systems with a bit rate of up to 2 Mbit/s

G.621   Characteristics of 0.7/2.9 mm coaxial cable pairs

G.622   Characteristics of 1.2/2.4 mm coaxial cable pairs

G.623   Characteristics of 2.6/9.5 mm coaxial cable pairs

G.631   Types of submarine cable to be used for systems with line frequencies of less than about 45 MHz

G.641   Waveguide diameters

G.651   Characteristics of 50/125 fm multimode graded index optical fibre cables

G.652   Characteristics of a single-mode optical fibre cable

G.700   General aspects of digital transmission systems - terminal equipments

G.701   Framework of the Series G.700, G.800 and G.900 Recommendations

G.702   Digital hierarchy bit rates

G.703   Physical/electrical characteristics of hierarchical digital interfaces

G.704   Functional characteristics of interfaces associated with network nodes

G.705   Characteristics required to terminate digital links on a digital exchange

G.706   Frame alignment and CRC procedures relating to basic frame structures defined in Recommendation G.704

G.711   Pulse code modulation (PCM) of voice frequencies

G.712   Performance characteristics of PCM channels between 4-wire interfaces at voice frequencies

G.713   Performance characteristics of PCM channels between 2-wire interfaces at voice frequencies

G.714   Separate performance characteristics for the send and receive sides of PCM channels applicable to 4-wire voice-frequency interfaces

G.721   32 kbit/s adaptive differential pulse code modulation (ADPCM)

G.722   7 KHz audio-coding within 64 Kbit/s

G.731   Primary PCM multiplex equipment for voice frequencies

G.732   Characteristics of primary PCM multiplex equipment operating at 2048 kbit/s

G.733   Characteristics of primary PCM multiplex equipment operating at 1544 Kbit/s

G.734   Characteristics of synchronous digital multipiex equipment operating at 1544 Kbit/s

G.735   Characteristics of primary PCM multiplex equipment operating at 2048 kbit/s and offering digital access at 384 kbit/s and/or synchronous digital access at 64 kbit/s

G.736   Characteristics of a synchronous digital multiplex equipment operating at 2048 kbit/s

G.737   Characteristics of an external access equipment operating at 2048 kbit/s offering digital access at 384 kbit/s and/or synchronous digital access at 64 kbit/s

G.741   General considerations on second order multiplex equipments

G.742   Second order digital multiplex equipment operating at 8448 kbit/s and using positive justification

G.743   Second order digital multiplex equipment operating at 6312 kbit/s and using positive justification

G.744   Second order PCM multiplex equipment operating at 8448 kbit/s

G.745   Second order digital multiplex equipment operating at 8448 kbit/s and using positive/zero/negative justification

G.746   Characteristics of second order PCM multiplex equipment operating at 6312 kbit/s

G.747   Second order digital multiplex equipment operating at 6312 kbit/s and multiplexing three tributaries at 2048 Kbit/s

G.751   Digital multiplex equipments operating at the third order bit rate of 34 368 kbit/s and the fourth order bit rate of 139 264 kbit/s and using positive justification

G.752   Characteristics of digital multiplex equipments based on a second order bit rate of 6312 Kbit/s and using positive justification

G.753   Third order digital multiplex equipment operating at 34 368 Kbit/s and using positive/zero/negative justification

G.754   Fourth order digital multiplex equipment operating at 139 264 Kbit/s and using positive/zero/negative justification

G.755   Digital multiplex equipment operating at 139 264 Kbit/s and multiplexing three tributaries at 44 736 Kbit/s

G.761   General characteristics of a 60-channel transcoder equipment

G.791   General considerations on transmultiplexing equipments

G.792   Characteristics common to all transmultiplexing equipments

G.793   Characteristics of 60-channel transmultiplexing equipments

G.794   Characteristics of 24-channel transmultiplexing equipments

G.795   Characteristics of codecs for FDM assemblies

G.801   Digital transmission models

G.802   Interconnection of digital paths using different techniques

G.803   Maintenance of digital networks

G.811   Timing requirements at the outputs of reference clocks and network nodes suitable for plesiochronous operation of international digital links

G.821   Error performance on an international digital connection forming part of an ISDN

G.822   Controlled slip rate objectives on an international digital connection

G.823   The control of jitter and wander within digital networks which are based on the 2048 kbit/s hierarchy

G.824   The control of jitter and wander within digital networks which are based on the 1544 kbit/s hierarchy

G.901   General considerations on digital sections and digital line systems

G.911   Digital line sections at 1544 Kbit/s

G.912   Digital line sections at 6312 Kbit/s

G.913   Digital line sections at 32064 Kbit/s

G.914   Digital line sections at 44736 Kbit/s

G.915   Digital line sections at 97728 Kbit/s

G.921   Digital sections based on the 2048 kbit/s hierarchy

G.931   Digital line sections at 3152 Kbit/s

G.941   Digital line systems provided by FDM transmission bearers

G.950   General considerations on digital line systems

G.951   Digital line systems based on the 1544 Kbit/s hierarchy on symmetric pair cables

G.952   Digital line systems based on the 2048 kbit/s hierarchy on symmetric pair cables

G.953   Digital line systems based on the 1544 kbit/s hierarchy on coaxial pair cables

G.954   Digital line systems based on the 2048 kbit/s hierarchy on coaxial pair cables

G.955   Digital line systems based on the 1544 kbit/s hierarchy on optical fibre cables

G.956   Digital line systems based on the 2048 kbit/s hierarchy on optical fibre cables

H-Series Recommendations

H.11   Characteristics of circuits in the switched telephone network

H.12   Characteristics of telephone-type leased circuits

H.13   Characteristics of an impulsive noise measuring instrument for telephone-type circuits

H.14   Characteristics of group links for the transmission of wide spectrum signals

H.15   Characteristics of supergroup links for the transmission of wide spectrum signals

H.16   Characteristics of an impulsive-noise measuring instrument for wideband data transmission

H.21   Composition and terminology of international voice-frequency telegraph systems

H.23   Basic characteristics of telegraph equipments used in international voice-frequency telegraph systems

H.32   Simultaneous communication by telephony and telegraphy on a telephone-type circuit

H.34   Subdivision of the frequency band of a telephone-type circuit between telegraphy and other services

H.41   Phototelegraph transmissions on telephone-type circuits

H.42   Range of phototelegraph transmissions on a telephone-type circuit

H.43   Document facsimile transmissions on leased telephone-type circuits

H.51   Power levels for data transmission over telephone lines

H.52   Transmission of wide-spectrum signals (data, facsimile etc.) on wideband group links

H.53   Transmission of wide-spectrum signals (data etc.) over wideband supergroup links

H.100   Visual telephone systems

H.110   Hypothetical reference connections for video-conferencing using primary digital group transmission

H.120   Codecs for videoconferencing using primary digital group transmission

H.130   Frame structures for use in the international inter-connection of digital codecs for videoconferencing or visual telephony

I-Series Recommendations

I.110   General structure of the I-series Recommendations and CCITT draft Recommendations

I.110   General structure of the I-series Recommendations

I.111   Relationship with other Recommendations relevant to ISDNs

I.112   Vocabulary of terms for ISDNs

I.120   Integrated Services Digital Networks

I.130   Attributes for the characterization of telecommunication services supported by an ISDN and network capabilities of an ISDN

I.210   Principles of telecommunication services supported by an ISDN

I.461   Support of X.21 and X.21*bis* based DTEs by an ISDN (X.30)

I.462   Support of Packet Mode Terminal equipment by an ISDN (X.31)

I.463   Support of DTEs with V-series type interfaces by an ISDN (V.110)

I.464   Rate adaption, multiplexing and support of existing interfaces for restricted 64 kbit/s transfer capability

M-Series Recommendations

M.10   General recommendation concerning maintenance

M.15   Maintenance considerations for new systems

M.20   Maintenance philosophy for analogue, digital and mixed networks

M.22   Principles for using alarm information for maintenance of international transmission systems and equipment

M.24   Principles for application of maintenance information for performance monitoring on international transmission systems and equipment

M.25   Line-up and maintenance limits

M.50   Vocabulary

M.70   Guiding principles on the general maintenance organisation for telephone-type international circuits

M.75   Technical service

M.80   Control stations

M.90   Sub-control stations

M.460   Bringing international group, supergroup etc. links into service

M.465   Bringing international digital blocks, paths and sections into service

M.470   Setting up and lining up analogue channels for international services

M.475   Setting up and lining up mixed analogue/digital channels for international services

M.480   Setting up and initially testing digital channels on an international digital path or block

M.490   Exchange of information for planned outages of transmission systems

M.495   Transmission path restoration for service protection

M.500   Routine maintenance measurements to be made on regulated line sections

M.510   Readjustment to the nominal value of a regulated line section (on a symmetric pair line, a coaxial line or a radio-relay link)

M.520   Routine maintenance on international group, supergroup, etc. links

M.530   Readjustment to the nominal value of an international group, supergroup, etc. link

M.535   Special maintenance procedures for multiple destination, unidirectional (MU) group and supergroup links

M.540   Routine maintenance of carrier and pilot generating equipment

M.560   International telephone circuits - principles, definitions and relative transmission levels

M.562   Types of circuit and circuit section

M.719   Testing point (switching and inter-register signalling)

M.720   Network analysis point

M.721   System availability information point

M.722   Network management point

M.723   Circuit control station

M.724   Circuit sub-control station

M.725   Restoration control point

M.726   Maintenance organisation for the wholly digital international automatic and semi-automatic telephone service

M.729   Organisation of the maintenance of international public switched telephone circuits used for data transmission

M.730   Maintenance methods

M.731   Subjective testing

M.732   Signalling and switching routine maintenance tests and measurements

M.733   Transmission routine maintenance measurements on automatic and semi-automatic circuits

M.734   Exchange of information on incoming test facilitiies at international switching centres

M.750   Inter-administrations agreements on Common Channel Signalling System No 6

M.760   Transfer link for Common Channel Signalling System No 6

M.761   Setting up and lining up a transfer link for Common Channel Signalling System No 6 (analogue versions)

M.762   Maintenance of Common Channel Signalling System No 6

M.800   Use of circuits for voice-frequence telegraphy

M.810   Setting up and lining up an international voice-frequency telegraph link for public telegraph circuits (for 50, 100 and 200 baud modulation rates)

M.820   Periodicity of routine tests on international voice-frequency telegraph links

M.830   Routine measurements to be made on international voice-frequency telegraph links

M.850   International time division multiplex (TDM) telegraph systems

M.880   International phototelegraph transmission

M.900   Use of leased group and supergroup links for wide-spectrum signal transmission (data, facsimile, etc.)

M.910   Setting up and lining up an international leased group link for wide-spectrum signal transmission

M.1010   Constitution and nomenclature of international leased circuits

M.1012   Circuit control station for leased and special circuits

M.1013   Sub-control station for leased and special circuits

M.1014   Transmission Maintenance Point (International Line)(TMP-IL)

M.1015   Types of transmission on leased circuits

M.1016   Assessment of the service availability performance of international leased circuits

M.1020   Characteristics of special quality international leased circuits, with special bandwidth conditioning

M.1025   Characteristics of special quality international leased circuits with basic bandwidth conditioning

M.1030   Characteristics of ordinary quality international leased circuits forming part of private switched telephone networks

M.1040   Characteristics of ordinary quality international leased circuits

M.1045   Preliminary exchange of information for the provision of international leased circuits

M.1050   Lining up an international point-to-point leased circuit

M.1055   Lining up an international multiterminal leased circuit

M.1060   Maintenance of international leased circuits

M.1100   General maintenance aspects of maritime satellite systems

M.1110   Maintenance organisation for the maritime satellite service

M.1120   Functions, maintenance responsibilities and maintenance facilities of a coast earth station for telephony services

M.1220   Network maintenance information

M.1230   Assessment of the performance of the international telephone network

M.1235   Use of automatically generated test calls for assessment of network performance

M.1300   International data transmission systems operating in the range 2400 bit/s to 64 Kbit/s

M.1320   Numbering of channels in data transmission systems

M.1350   Setting up, lining up and characteristics of international data transmission systems operating in the range 2.4 Kbit/s to 9.6 Kbit/s

M.1355   Maintenance of international data transmission systems operating in the range 2.4 Kbit/s to 9.6 Kbit/s

M.1370   Setting up and lining up of international data transmission systems operating in the range 48 Kbit/s to 64 Kbit/s

M.1375   Maintenance of international data transmission systems operating in the range 48 Kbit/s to 64 Kbit/s

Q-Series Recommendations

Q.1   Signal receivers for manual working

Q.4   Automatic switching functions for use in national networks

Q.5   Advantages of semi-automatic service in the international telephone service

Q.6   Advantages of international automatic working

Q.7   Signalling systems to be used for international automatic and semi-automatic telephone working

Q.8   Signalling systems to be used for international manual and automatic working on analogue leased circuits

Q.9   Vocabulary of switching and signalling terms

Q.10   Definitions relating to national and international numbering plans

Q.11bis   Numbering plan for the international telephone service

Q.12   Overflow - alternative routing - rerouting - automatic repeat attempt

Q.13   International telephone routing plan

Q.14   Means to control the number of satellite links in an international telephone connection

Q.15   Nominal mean power during the busy hour

Q.107   Standard sending sequence of forward address information

Q.107bis   Standard sending sequence of forward address information

Q.108   One-way or both-way operation of international circuits

Q.109   Transmission of the answer signal in international exchanges

Q.110   General aspects of the utilization of standardized CCITT signalling systems on PCM links

Q.112   Signal levels and signal receiver sensitivity

Q.113   Connection of signal receivers in the circuit

Q.114   Typical transmission requirements for signal senders and receivers

Q.115   Control of echo suppressors

Q.116   Indication given to the outgoing operator or calling subscriber in case of an abnormal condition

Q.117   Alarms for technical staff and arrangements in case of faults

Q.118   Special release arrangements

Q.118bis   Indication of congestion conditions at transit exchanges

Q.120   Definition and function of signals

Q.121   Signal code

Q.122   Signal sender

Q.123   Signal receiver

Q.124   Splitting arrangements

Q.125   Speed of switching in international exchanges

Q.297	Network management
Q.300	Interworking between CCITT Signalling System No 6 and national Common Channel signalling systems
Q.310	Definition and function of signals
Q.311	2600 Hz line signalling
Q.312	2600 Hz line signal sender (transmitter)
Q.313	2600 Hz line signal receiving equipment
Q.314	PCM line signalling
Q.315	PCM line signal sender (transmitter)
Q.316	PCM line signal receiver
Q.317	Further specification clauses relative to line signalling
Q.318	Double seizing with both-way operation to line signalling
Q.319	Speed of switching in international exchanges
Q.320	Signal code for register signalling
Q.321	End-of-pulsing conditions - register arrangements concerning ST signal
Q.322	Multifrequency signal sender
Q.323	Multifrequency signal receiving equipment
Q.324	Analysis of address information for routing
Q.325	Release of registers
Q.326	Switching to the speech position
Q.327	Testing arrangement - general arrangements
Q.328	Routing testing of equipment (local maintenance)
Q.329	Manual testing

Q.607   Interworking requirements for new signalling systems

Q.608   Miscellaneous interworking aspects

Q.611-Q.685 [Logic procedures for various Signalling Systems]

Q.701   Signalling System No 7 - Message Transfer Part (MTP) - Functional description

Q.702   Signalling System No 7 - Message Transfer Part (MTP) - Signalling data link

Q.703   Signalling System No 7 - Message Transfer Part (MTP) - Signalling link

Q.704   Signalling System No 7 - Message Transfer Part (MTP) - Signalling network functions and messages

Q.705   Signalling System No 7 - Message Transfer Part (MTP) - Signalling network structure

Q.706   Signalling System No 7 - Message Transfer Part (MTP) - MTP performance

Q.707   Signalling System No 7 - Message Transfer Part (MTP) - Testing and maintenance

Q.708   Signalling System No 7 - Message Transfer Part (MTP) - Numbering of international signalling point codes

Q.709   Signalling System No 7 - Message Transfer Part (MTP) - Hypothetical signalling reference connection

Q.710   Use of Signalling System No 7 for PABX application

Q.711   Signalling System No 7 - Signalling Connection Control Part (SCCP) - Functional description of the SCCP

Q.712   Signalling System No 7 - Signalling Connection Control Part (SCCP) - Definition of functions of SCCP messages

Q.713   Signalling System No 7 - Signalling Connection Control Part (SCCP) - SCCP formats and codes

Q.921   ISDN user-network interface data link layer specification (I.441)

Q.930   ISDN user-network interface layer 3 - general aspects (I.450)

Q.931   ISDN user-network interface layer 3 specification (I.451)

R-Series Recommendations

R.2   Element error rate

R.4   Methods for the separate measurements of the degrees of various types of telegraph distortion

R.5   Observation conditions recommended for routine distortion measurements on international telegraph circuits

R.9   How the laws governing distribution of distortion should be arrived at

R.11   Calculation of the degree of distortion of a telegraph circuit in terms of the degrees of distortion of the component links

R.20   Telegraph modem for subscriber lines

R.30   Transmission characteristics for international VFT links

R.31   Standardization of AMVFT systems for a modulation rate of 50 bauds

R.35   Standardization of FMVFT systems for a modulation rate of 50 bauds

R.35bis   50-baud wideband VFT systems

R.36   Coexistence of 50-baud/120 Hz channels, 100-baud/240 Hz channels, 200-baud/360 Hz channels on the same voice-frequency telegraph system

R.37	Standardization of FMVFT systems for a modulation rate of 100 bauds
R.38A	Standardization of FMVFT systems for a modulation rate of 200 bauds with channels spaced at 480 Hz
R.38B	Standardization of FMVFT systems for a modulation rate of 200 bauds with channels spaced at 360 Hz usable on long intercontinental bearer circuits generally used with a 3 kHz spacing
R.39	Voice-frequency telegraphy on radio circuits
R.40	Coexistence in the same cable of telephony and supra-acoustic telegraphy
R.43	Simultaneous communication by telephone and telegraph on a telephone-type circuit
R.44	6-unit synchronous time-division 2-3 channel multiplex telegraph system for use over FMVFT channels spaced at 120 Hz for connection to standardsized teleprinter networks
R.49	Interband telegraphy over open-wire 3-channel carrier systems
R.50	Tolerable limits for the degree of isochronous distortion of code-independent 50-baud telegraph circuits
R.51	Standardized text for distortion testing of the code-independent elements of a complete circuit
R.51bis	Standardized text for testing the elements of a complete circuit
R.52	Standardization of international texts for the measurement of the margin of start-stop equipment
R.53	Permissible limits for the degree of distortion on an international 50-baud/120 Hz VFT channel (frequency and amplitude modulation)
R.54	Conventional degree of distortion tolerable for standardized start-stop 50-baud systems

R.55   Conventional degree of distortion

R.57   Standard limits of transmission quality for planning code-independent international point-to-point telegraph communications and switched networks using 50-baud start-stop equipment

R.58   Standard limits of transmission quality for the Gentex and Telex networks

R.58bis   Limits on signal transfer delay for telegraph, Telex and Gentex networks

R.59   Interface requirements for 50-baud start-stop telegraph transmission in the maritime mobile satellite service

R.60   Conditions to be fulfilled by regenerative repeaters for start-stop signals of International Telegraph Alphabet No 2

R.62   Siting of regenerative repeaters in international Telex circuits

R.70   Designation of international Telex circuits

R.70bis   Numbering of international VFT channels

R.71   Organization of the maintenance of international telegraph circuits

R.72   Periodicity of maintenance measurements to be carried out on the channels of international VFT systems

R.73   Maintenance measurements to be carried out on VFT systems

R.74   Choice of type of telegraph distortion measuring equipment

R.75   Maintenance measurements on code-independent international sections of international telegraph circuits

R.75bis   Maintenance measurements of character error rate on international sections of international telegraph circuits

R.76	Reserve channels for maintenance measurements on channels of international VFT systems
R.77	Use of bearer circuits for voice-frequency telegraphy
R.78	Pilot channel for AMVFT systems
R.79	Automatic tests of transmission quality on telegraph circuits between switching centres where no regeneration is involved
R.79bis	Automatic tests of transmission quality on telegraph circuits between switching centres where regeneration is involved
R.80	Causes of disturbances to signals in VFT channels and their effect on telegraph distortion
R.81	Maximum acceptable limit for the duration of interruption of telegraph channels arising from failure of the normal power supplies
R.82	Appearance of false calling and clearing signals in circuits operated by switched teleprinter services
R.83	Changes of level and interruptions in VFT channels
R.90	Organization for locating and clearing faults in international telegraph switched circuits
R.91	General maintenance aspects for the maritime satellite Telex service
R.100	Transmission characteristics of international TDM links
R.101	Code and speed dependent TDM system for anisochronous telegraph and data transmission using bit interleaving
R.102	4800 bit/s code and speed dependent and hybrid TDM systems for anisochronous telegraph and data transmission using bit interleaving
R.105	Duplex statistical muldex connecting a group of Gentex and Telex subscribers to a telegraph exchange by

assigning virtual channels to time slots of a bit-interleaved TDM system

R.111 Code and speed independent TDM system for anisochronous telegraph and data transmission

R.112 TDM hybrid system for anisochronous telegraph and data transmission using bit interleaving

R.114 Numbering of international TDM channels

R.115 Maintenance loops for TDM systems

R.120 Tolerable limits for the degree of isochronous distortion of code-independent telegraph circuits operating at modulation rates of 75, 100 and 200 bauds

R.121 Standard limits of transmission quality for start-stop user classes of service 1 and 2 on anisochronous data network

R.140 Definitions of essential technical terms in the field of telegraph transmission

R.150 Automatic protection switching of dual diversity bearers

S-Series Recommendations

S.1 International telegraph alphabet No 2

S.3 Transmission characteristics of the local end with its termination (ITA No 2)

S.4 Special use of certain characters of the International Telegraph Alphabet No 2

S.5 Standardization of page-printing start-stop equipment and cooperation between page-printing and tape-printing start-stop equipment (ITA No 2)

S.6 Characteristics of answer-back units (ITA No 2)

S.7 Control of teleprinter motors

S.8	Intercontinental standardization of the modulation rate of start-stop apparatus and of the use of combination No 4 in figure case
S.9	Switching equipment of start-stop apparatus
S.10	Transmission at reduced character transfer rate over a standardized 50-baud telegraph channel
S.11	Use of start-stop reperforating equipment for perforated tape retransmission
S.12	Conditions that must be satisfied by synchronous systems operating in connection with standard 50-baud teleprinter circuits
S.13	Use of radio circuits of 7-unit synchronous systems giving error correction by automatic repetition
S.14	Suppression of unwanted reception in radiotelegraph multi-destination teleprinter systems
S.15	Use of the telex network for data transmission at 50 bauds
S.16	Connection to the telex network of an automatic terminal using a V.24 DCE/DTE interface
S.17	Answer-back unit simulators
S.18	Conversion between International Telegraph Alphabet No 2 and International Alphabet No 5
S.19	Calling and answering in the telex network with automatic terminal equipment
S.20	Automatic clearing procedure for a telex terminal
S.21	Use of display screens in telex machines
S.22	Use of "conversation impossible" response to J/BELL signals from a telex terminal
S.30	Standardization of basic model page-printing machine using International Alphabet No 5

S.31   Characteristics, from the transmission point of view, at the interchange point between data terminal equipment and data circuit-terminating equipment when a 200 baud start-stop data terminal equipment in accordance with International Alphabet

S.32   Answer-back units for 200- and 300-baud start-stop machines in accordance with Recommendation S.30

S.33   Standardization of an international text for the measurement of the margin of start-stop machines using International Alphabet No 5

S.140   Definitions of essential technical terms relating to apparatus for alphabetic telegraphy

T-Series Recommendations

T.0   Classification of facsimile apparatus for document transmission over the public networks

T.1   Standardization of phototelegraph apparatus

T.2   Standardization of Group 1 facsimile apparatus for document transmission

T.3   Standardization of Group 2 facsimile apparatus for document transmission

T.4   Standardisation of Group 3 facsimile apparatus for document transmission

T.5   General aspects of Group 4 facsimile apparatus

T.6   Facsimile coding scheme and coding control functions for Group 4 facsimile apparatus

T.10   Document facsimile transmissions on leased telephone-type circuits

T.10bis   Document facsimile transmissions in the general switched telephone network

T.11   Phototelegraph transmissions on telephone-type circuit

T.12   Range of phototelegraph transmissions on a telephone-type circuit

T.15   Phototelegraph transmission over combined radio and metallic circuits

T.18   Conversion between alphabets ITA2 and IA5

T.20   Standardized test chart for facsimile transmissions

T.21   Standardized test chart for document facsimile transmissions

T.30   Procedures for facsimile document transmission over the Public Switched Telephone Network

T.35   Procedure for the allocation of CCITT members' codes

T.50   International Alphabet No 5

T.51   Coded character sets for Telematic services

T.60   Terminal equipment for use in the Teletex service

T.61   Character repertoire and coded character sets for the international Teletex service

T.62   Control procedures for the Teletex and Group 4 facsimile services

T.63   Provisions for verification of Teletex terminal compliance

T.70   Network-independent basic transport service for the Telematic services

T.71   LAP-B extended for half-duplex physical link facility

T.72   Terminal capabilities for mixed mode of operation

T.73   Document interchange protocol for the Telematic services

T.90   Teletex requirements for interworking with the telex
                  service

T.91   Teletex requirements for real-time interworking with the
                  telex service in a packet-switching network
                  environment

T.100   International information exchange for interactive
                  Videotex

T.101   International interworking for Videotex service

T.101 AnnB   Data syntax I for international interactive Videotex
                  service

T.101 AnnC   Data syntax II for international interactive Videotex
                  service

T.101 AnnD   Data syntax III for international interactive Videotex
                  service

V-Series Recommendations

V.1   Equivalence between binary notation symbols and the
                  significant conditions of a two condition code

V.2   Power levels for data transmission over telephone lines

V.4   General structure of signals of International Alphabet
                  No 5 for data and message transmission over public
                  telephone networks

V.5   Standardisation of modulation rates and data signalling
                  for synchronous data transmission in the general
                  switched telephone network

V.6   Standardisation of modulation rates and data signalling
                  rates for synchronous data transmission on leased
                  telephone-type circuits

V.7   Definition of terms concerning data communication
                  over the telephone network

V.10 Electrical characteristics for unbalanced double-current interchange circuits for general use with integrated circuit equipment in the field of data communications (X.26)

V.11 Electrical characteristics for balanced double-current interchange circuits for general use with integrated circuit equipment in the field of data communications (X.27)

V.15 Use of acoustic coupling for data transmission

V.16 Medical analogue data transmission modems

V.19 Modems for parallel data transmission using telephone signalling frequencies

V.20 Parallel data transmission modems standardized for universal use in the general switched telephone network

V.21 300 bit/s duplex modem standardized for use in the general switched telephone network

V.22 1200 bit/s duplex modem standardized for use in the general switched telephone network and on point-to-point 2-wire leased telephone-type circuits

V.22bis 2400 bit/s duplex modem using the frequency division technique standardized for use on the general switched telephone network and on point-to-point 2-wire leased telephone-type circuits

V.23 600/1200 bit/s modem standardized for use in the general switched telephone network

V.24 List of definitions for interchange circuits between Data Terminal Equipment and Data Circuit Terminating Equipment

V.25 Automatic answering equipment and/or parallel automatic calling equipment on the general switched telephone network including procedures for disabling of echo control devices for both manually and automatic established calls

V.25bis   Automatic calling and/or answering equipment on the General Switched Telephone Network (GSTN) using the 100-series interchange circuits

V.26   2400 bit/s modem standardized for use on 4-wire leased telephone-type circuits

V.26bis   2400/1200 bit/s modem standardized for use in the general switched telephone network

V.26ter   2400 bit/s duplex modem using the echo cancellation technique standardized for use on the general switched telephone network and on point-to-point 2-wire leased telephone-type circuits

V.27   4800 bit/s modem with manual equalizer standardized for use on leased telephone-type circuits

V.27bis   4800/2400 bit/s modem with automatic equalizer standardized for use on leased telephone-type circuits

V.27ter   4800/2400 bit/s modem standardized for use in the general switched telephone network

V.28   Electrical characteristics for unbalanced double-current interchange circuits

V.29   9600 bit/s modem standardized for use on point-to-point 4-wire leased telephone-type circuits

V.30   Parallel data transmission systems for universal use on the general switched telephone network

V.31   Electrical characteristics for single-current interchange circuits controlled by contact closure

V.31bis   Electrical characteristics for single-current interchange circuits using opto-couplers

V.32   A family of 2-wire duplex modems operating at data signalling rates of up to 9600 bit/s for use on the general switched telephone network and on leased telephone-type circuits

V.33   14400 bit/s modem standardized for use on point-to-point 4-wire leased telephone-type circuits

V.35   Data transmission at 48 kilobits per second using 60-108 kHz group band circuits

V.36   Modems for synchronous data transmission using 60-108 kHz group band circuits

V.37   Synchronous data transmission at a data signalling rate higher than 72 kbits per second using 60-108 kHz group band circuits

V.40   Error indication with electro-mechanical equipment

V.41   Code independent error control system

V.50   Standard limits for transmission quality of data transmission

V.51   Organisation of the maintenance of international telephone-type circuits used for data transmission

V.52   Characteristics of distortion and error rate measuring apparatus for data transmission

V.53   Limits for the maintenance of telephone-type circuits used for data transmission

V.54   Loop test device for modems

V.55   Specification for an impulsive noise measuring instrument for telephone-type circuits

V.56   Comparative tests of modems for use over telephone-type circuits

V.57   Comprehensive data test set for high data signalling rates

V.100 Interconnection between Public Data Networks (PDNs) and Public Switched Telephone Network (PSTN)

V.110   Support of DTEs with V-series type interfaces by an ISDN (I.463)

X-Series Recommendations

X.1   International user classes of service in public data networks and Integrated Services Digital Networks (ISDNs)

X.2   International user services and facilities in public data networks and ISDNs

X.3   Packet assembly/disassembly facility (PAD) in a public data network

X.4   General structure of signals of International Alphabet No 5 code for character oriented data transmission over public data networks

X.10   Categories of access for Data Terminal Equipment (DTE) to Public Data Transmission Services provided by PDNs and ISDNs through terminal adaptors

X.15   Definitions of terms concerning public data networks

X.20   Interface between data terminal equipment (DTE) and data circuit-terminating equipment (DCE) for start-stop transmission services on public data networks

X.20bis   Use on public data networks of data terminal equipment (DTE) which is designed for interfacing to asynchronous duplex V-series modems

X.21   Interface between data terminal equipment (DTE) and data circuit-terminating equipment (DCE) for synchronous operation on public data networks

X.21bis   Use on public data networks of data terminal equipment (DTE) which is designed for interfacing to synchronous V-series modems

X.22   Multiplex DTE/DCE interface for user classes 3-6

X.24   List of definitions for interchange circuits between data terminal equipment (DTE) and data circuit-terminating equipment (DCE) on public data networks

X.25   Interface between data terminal equipment (DTE) and data circuit-terminating equipment (DCE) for terminals operating in the packet mode and connected to public data networks by dedicated circuit

X.26   Electrical characteristics for unbalanced double-current interchange circuits for general use with integrated circuit equipment in the field of data communications (V.10)

X.27   Electrical characteristics for balanced double-current interchange circuits for general use with integrated circuit equipment in the field of data communications (V.11)

X.28   DTE/DCE interface for a start-stop mode data terminal equipment accessing the packet assembly/disassembly facility (PAD) in a public data network situated in the same country

X.29   Procedures for the exchange of control information and user data between a packet assembly/disassembly (PAD) facility and a packet mode DTE or another PAD

X.30   Support of X.21, X.21*bis* and X.20*bis* based data terminal equipments (DTEs) by an integrated services digital network (ISDN) (I.461)

X.31   Support of packet mode terminal equipment by an ISDN (I.462)

X.32   Interface between data terminal equipment (DTE) and data circuit-terminating equipment (DCE) for terminals operating in the packet mode and accessing a packet switched data network through a public switched telephone network or a circuit swit

X.40   Standardisation of frequency-shift modulated transmission systems for the provision of telegraph and data channels by frequency division of a primary group

X.50   Fundamental parameters of a multiplexing scheme for the international interface between synchronous data networks

X.50bis   Fundamental parameters of a 48 kbit/s user data signalling rate transmission scheme for the international interface between synchronous data networks

X.51   Fundamental parameters of a multiplexing scheme for the international interface between synchronous data networks using 10-bit envelope structure

X.51bis   Fundamental parameters of a 48 kbit/s user data signalling rate transmission scheme for the international interface between synchronous data networks using 10-bit envelope structure

X.52   Method of encoding anisochronous signals into a synchronous user bearer

X.53   Numbering of channels on international multiplex links at 64 kbit/s

X.54   Allocation of channels on international multiplex links at 64 kbit/s

X.55   Interface between synchronous data networks using a 6 + 2 envelope structure and single channel per carrier (SCPC) satellite channels

X.56   Interface between synchronous data networks using an 8 + 2 envelope structure and single channel per carrier (SCPC) satellite channels

X.57   Method of transmitting a single lower speed data channel on a 64 kbit/s data stream

X.60   Common channel signalling for synchronous data applications - data user part

X.61   Signalling System No 7 - Data User Part (Q.741)

X.70   Terminal and transit control signalling system for start-stop services on international circuits between anisochronous data networks

X.71   Decentralised terminal and transit control signalling system on international circuits between synchronous data networks

X.75   Terminal and transit call control procedures and data transfer systems on international circuits between packet-switched data networks

X.80   Interworking of interexchange signalling systems for circuit switched data services

X.87   Principles and procedures for realization of international user facilities and network utilities in public data networks

X.92   Hypothetical reference connections for public synchronous data networks

X.93   Hypothetical reference connection for packet switched data transmission services

X.95   Network parameters in public data networks

X.96   Call progress signals in public data networks

X.110   Routing principles for international public data services through switched public data networks of the same type

X.121   International numbering plan for public data networks

X.130   Call processing delays in public data networks when providing international synchronous circuit-switched data service

X.131   Call blocking in public data networks when providing international synchronous circuit switched data service

X.132   Provisional objectives for grade of service in international data communications over circuit switched public data networks

X.135   Delay aspects of grade of service for public data networks when providing international packet-switched data services

X.136   Blocking aspects of grade of service for public data networks when providing international packet-switched data service

X.141   General principles for the detection and correction of errors in public data networks

X.150   Principles of maintenance testing for public data networks using data terminal equipment (DTE) and data circuit-terminating equipment (DCE) test loops

X.180   Administrative arrangements for international closed user groups (CUG)

X.181   Administrative arrangements for the provision of international permanent virtual circuits (PVCs)

X.200   Reference Model of Open Systems Interconnection for CCITT applications

X.210   Layer Service Conventions of OSI for CCITT applications

X.224   Transport Protocol Specification of OSI for CCITT applications

X.225   Connection Oriented Session Protocol specification for OSI for CCITT applications

X.244   Procedure for the exchange of protocol identification during virtual call establishment on packet switched public data networks

X.250   Formal description techniques for data communications protocols and services

X.300   General principles and arrangements for interworking between Public Data Networks and other networks

X.310 Procedures and arrangements for Data Terminal Equipments accessing circuit switched digital data services through analogue telephone networks

X.350 General requirements to be met for data transmission in the maritime satellite service

X.351 Special requirements to be met for packet assembly/disassembly facilities (PADs) located at or in association with coast earth stations in the maritime satellite service

X.352 Interworking between public packet switched data networks and the maritime satellite data transmission system

X.353 Routing principles for interconnecting international mobile satellite data transmission systems with public data networks

X.400 Message Handling Systems: System Model - Service Elements

X.401 Message Handling Systems: basic service elements and optional user facilities

X.408 Message Handling Systems: encoded information type conversion rules

X.409 Message Handling Systems: Presentation transfer syntax and notation

X.410 Message Handling Systems: remote operations and reliable transfer server

X.411 Message Handling Systems: Message Transfer Layer

X.420 Message Handling Systems: interpersonal messaging User Agent Layer

X.430 Message Handling Systems: Access protocol for Teletex terminals

Z-Series Recommendations

Z.100	Introduction to the specification and description language (SDL)
Z.101	General explanation of the specification and description language (SDL)
Z.102	Structural concepts in SDL
Z.103	Functional extensions to SDL
Z.104	Data in SDL
Z.200	CCITT High Level Language (CHILL)
Z.301	Introduction to the CCITT man-machine language
Z.302	The meta-language for describing MML syntax and dialogue procedures
Z.311	Introduction to syntax and dialogue procedures
Z.312	Basic format layout
Z.314	The character set and basic elements
Z.315	Input (command) language syntax specification
Z.316	Output language syntax specification
Z.317	Man-machine dialogue procedures
Z.321	Introduction to the extended MML for visual display terminals
Z.322	Capabilities of visual display terminals
Z.323	Man-machine interaction
Z.331	Introduction to the specification of the man-machine interface
Z.332	Methodology for the specification of the man-machine interface - general working procedure

Z.333   Methodology for the specification of the man-machine interface - tools and methods

Z.341   Glossary of terms

1.2   1988 CCITT RECOMMENDATIONS

A-Series Recommendations

A.1   Presentation of contributions relative to the study of questions assigned to the CCITT

A.10   Terms and definitions

A.12   Collaboration with the International Electrotechnical Commission on the subject of definitions for telecommunications

A.13   Collaboration with the International Electrotechnical Commission on graphical symbols and diagrams used in telecommunications

A.14   Publication of definitions

A.15   Presentation of CCITT texts

A.20   Collaboration with other international organizations over data transmission

A.21   Collaboration with other international organizations on CCITT defined telematic services

A.22   Collaboration with other international organizations on information technology

A.30   Major degradation or disruption of service

D-Series Recommendations

D.10   General tariff principles for international public data communication services

D.11   Special tariff principles for international packet-switched public data communication services by means of the virtual call facility

E-Series Recommendations

F-Series Recommendations

F.421   Intercommunication Telex/IPM service

F.422   Intercommunication Teletex/IPM service

F.500   International public directory services

I-Series Recommendations

I.110   General structure of the I-series Recommendations and
                 CCITT draft Recommendations

I.111   Relationship with other Recommendations relevant to
                 ISDNs

I.112   Vocabulary of terms for ISDNs

I.113   Vocabulary of terms for broadbanc aspects of ISDN

I.120   General ISDN concepts

I.121   Broadband aspects of ISDN

I.122   Framework for providing additional packet-mode
                 bearer services

I.130   Method for the characterization of telecommunication
                 services supported by an ISDN and network
                 capabilities of an ISDN

I.140   Attribute technique for the characterization of tele-
                 communication services supported by an ISDN and
                 network capabilities of an ISDN

I.141   ISDN network charging capabilities attributes

I.200   Guidance to the I.200 series of Recommendations

I.210   Principles of telecommunication services and the
                 means to describe them

I.220   Common dynamic description of basic tele-
                 communication services

I.221   Common specific characteristics of services

I.334   Principles relating ISDN numbers/subaddresses to the OSI Reference Model network layer addresses

I.335   ISDN routing principles

I.340   ISDN connection types

I.350   General aspects of quality of service and network performance in digital networks

I.351   Recommendations in other series concerning network performance objectives that apply at reference point T of an ISDN

I.352   Network performance objectives for connection processing delays in an ISDN

I.410   General aspects and principles relating to Recommendations on ISDN user-network interfaces

I.411   ISDN user-network interfaces - reference configurations

I.412   ISDN user-network interfaces - interface structures and access capabilities

I.420   Basic user-network interface

I.421   Primary rate user-network interface

I.430   Basic user-network interface - layer 1 specification

I.431   Primary rate user-network interface - layer 1 specification

I.440   ISDN user-network interface data link layer protocol - general aspects (Q.920)

I.441   ISDN user-network interface data link layer specification (Q.921)

I.450   ISDN user-network interface layer 3 general aspects (Q.930)

I.451   ISDN user-network interface layer 3 specification for basic call control (Q.931)

I.603   Application of maintenance principles to ISDN basic rate accesses

I.604   Application of maintenance principles to ISDN primary rate accesses

I.605   Application of maintenance principles to static multiplexed ISDN basic rate accesses

P-Series Recommendations

P.31   Transmission characteristics for digital telephones

P.51   Artificial mouths and artificial ears

P.79   Calculation of loudness ratings

Q-Series Recommendations

Q.65   Stage 2 of the method for the characterization of services supported by an ISDN

Q.71   ISDN 64 Kbit/s circuit mode switched bearer services

Q.701   Signalling System No 7 - Message Transfer Part (MTP) - Functional description

Q.702   Signalling System No 7 - Message Transfer Part (MTP) - Signalling data link

Q.703   Signalling System No 7 - Message Transfer Part (MTP) - Signalling link

Q.704   Signalling System No 7 - Message Transfer Part (MTP) - Signalling network functions and messages

Q.705   Signalling System No 7 - Message Transfer Part (MTP) - Signalling network structure

Q.706   Signalling System No 7 - Message Transfer Part (MTP) - MTP signalling performance

Q.707   Signalling System.No 7 - Message Transfer Part (MTP) - Testing and maintenance

Q.711   Signalling System No 7 - Signalling Connection Control Part (SCCP) - Functional description of the SCCP

Q.712   Signalling System No 7 - Signalling Connection Control Part (SCCP) - Definition and functions of SCCP messages

Q.713   Signalling System No 7 - Signalling Connection Control Part (SCCP) - SCCP formats and codes

Q.714   Signalling System No 7 - Signalling Connection Control Part (SCCP) - SCCP Procedures

Q.921   ISDN user-network interface data link layer specification (I.441)

Q.940   ISDN user-network interface protocol for management - General aspects

T-Series Recommendations

T.0   Classification of facsimile apparatus for document transmission over the public networks

T.1   Standardization of phototelegraph apparatus

T.2   Standardization of Group 1 facsimile apparatus for document transmission

T.3   Standardization of Group 2 facsimile apparatus for document transmission

T.4   Standardisation of Group 3 facsimile apparatus for document transmission

T.6   Facsimile coding scheme and coding control functions for Group 4 facsimile apparatus

T.10   Document facsimile transmissions on leased telephone-type circuits

T.10bis   Document facsimile transmissions in the general switched telephone network

T.20   Standardized test chart for facsimile transmissions

T.21   Standardized test chart for document facsimile transmissions

T.30   Procedures for facsimile document transmission in the general switched telephone network

T.35   Procedure for the allocation of CCITT members' codes

T.50   International Alphabet No 5

T.51   Coded character sets for Telematic services

T.60   Terminal equipment for use in the Teletex service

T.61   Character repertoire and coded character sets for the international Teletex service

T.62   Control procedures for the Teletex and Group 4 facsimile services

T.62bis   Control procedures for the Teletex and Group 4 facsimile services based on Recommendations X.215 and X.225

T.63   Provisions for verification of Teletex terminal compliance

T.64   Conformance testing procedures for the teletex Recommendations

T.65   Applicability of telematic protocols and terminal characteristics to computerized communication terminals (CCTs)

T.70   Network-independent basic transport service for the telematic services

T.71   Link access protocol balanced (LAP-B) extended for half-duplex physical level facility

T.80   New image communication (NIC)

T.90   Characteristics and protocols for terminals for Telematic services in ISDN

T.91   Teletex requirements for real-time interworking with the telex service in a packet-switching network environment

T.100   International information exchange for interactive Videotex

T.101   International interworking for Videotex service

T.101 AnnA   International information exchange for interactive Videotex - interworking data syntax

T.122   Audiographic system and terminal requirements

T.150   Telewriting terminal equipment
Part 1:   Fundamental characteristics
Part 2:   Telewriting together with telephony
Part 3:   Zone coding
Part 4:   Differential chain coding

T.300   General principles of telematic interworking

T.330   Telematic access to Interpersonal Messaging Systems (IPMS)

T.351   Imaging process of character information on facsimile apparatus

T.390   Teletex requirements for interworking with the Telex services

T.400   Document Transfer and Manipulation (DTAM) - General introduction

T.411   Open Document Architecture (ODA) and Interchange Format - Introduction and General Principles

T.412   Open Document Architecture (ODA) and Interchange Format - Document Structures

T.414   Open Document Architecture (ODA) and Interchange Format - Document Profile

T.415   Open Document Architecture (ODA) and Interchange Format - Open Document Interchange Format (ODIF)

T.416   Open Document Architecture (ODA) and Interchange Format - Character Content Architectures

T.417   Open Document Architecture (ODA) and Interchange Format - Raster Graphics Content Architectures

T.418   Open Document Architecture (ODA) and Interchange Format - Geometric Graphics Content Architectures

T.419   Document Transfer, Access and Manipulation (DTAM) - Composite Graphics Content Architectures

T.431   Document Transfer, Access and Manipulation (DTAM) - Services and Protocols - Introduction and General Principles

T.432   Document Transfer, Access and Manipulation (DTAM) - Services and Protocols - Service Definition

T.433   Document Transfer, Access and Manipulation (DTAM) - Services and Protocols - Protocol Specification

T.441   Document Transfer, Access and Manipulation (DTAM) - Operational Structure

T.501   Document Application Profile MM for the interchange of formatted mixed mode documents

T.502   Document Application Profile PM1 for the interchange of processable form documents

T.503   Document Application Profile for the interchange of Group 4 facsimile documents

T.504   Document Application Profile for videotex interworking

T.521   Communication Application Profile BT0 for document bulk transfer using the Session Service (according to the rules defined in Recommendation T.62*bis*)

T.522   Communication Application Profile BT1 for document bulk transfer

T.523   Communication Application Profile DM1 for videotex interworking

T.541   Operational Application Profile for videotex interworking

T.561   Terminal characteristics for mixed mode of operation MM

T.562   Terminal characteristics for teletex processable mode PM1

T.563   Terminal characteristics for Group 4 facsimile apparatus

T.564   Gateway characteristics for videotex interworking

V-Series Recommendations

V.1   Equivalence between binary notation symbols and the significant conditions of a two-condition code

V.2   Power levels for data transmission over telephone lines

V.4   General structure of signals of International Alphabet No 5 code for character oriented data transmission over public telephone networks

V.5   Standardisation of data signalling rates for synchronous data transmission in the general switched telephone network

V.6   Standardisation of data signalling rates for synchronous data transmission on leased telephone-type circuits

V.7   Definition of terms concerning data communication over the telephone network

V.10   Electrical characteristics for unbalanced double-current interchange circuits for general use with integrated circuit equipment in the field of data communications (X.26)

V.11   Electrical characteristics for balanced double-current interchange circuits for general use with integrated circuit equipment in the field of data communications (X.27)

V.13   Simulated carrier control

V.14   Transmission of start-stop characters over synchronous bearer channels

V.15   Use of acoustic coupling for data transmission

V.16   Medical analogue data transmission modems

V.19   Modems for parallel data transmission using telephone signalling frequencies

V.20   Parallel data transmission modems standardized for universal use in the general switched telephone network

V.21   300 bits per second duplex modem standardized for use in the general switched telephone network

V.22   1200 bits per second duplex modem standardized for use in the general switched telephone network and on point-to-point 2-wire leased telephone-type circuits

V.22bis   2400 bits per second duplex modem using the frequency division technique standardized for use on the general switched telephone network and on point-to-point 2-wire leased telephone-type circuits

V.23   600/1200-baud modem standardized for use in the general switched telephone network

V.24   List of definitions for interchange circuits between data terminal equipment (DTE) and data circuit-terminating equipment (DCE)

V.25   Automatic answering equipment and/or parallel automatic calling equipment on the general switched telephone network including procedures for disabling of echo control devices for both manually and automatic established calls

V.25bis   Automatic calling and/or answering equipment on the general switched telephone network (GSTN) using the 100-series interchange circuits

V.26   2400 bits per second modem standardized for use on 4-wire leased telephone-type circuits

V.26bis   2400/1200 bits per second modem standardized for use in the general switched telephone network

V.26ter   2400 bits per second duplex modem using the echo cancellation technique standardized for use on the general switched telephone network and on point-to-point 2-wire leased telephone-type circuits

V.27   4800 bits per second modem with manual equalizer standardized for use on leased telephone-type circuits

V.27bis   4800/2400 bits per second modem with automatic equalizer standardized for use on leased telephone-type circuits

V.27ter   4800/2400 bits per second modem standardized for use in the general switched telephone network

V.28   Electrical characteristics for unbalanced double-current interchange circuits

V.29   9600 bits per second modem standardized for use on point-to-point 4-wire leased telephone-type circuits

V.31   Electrical characteristics for single-current interchange circuits controlled by contact closure

V.31bis   Electrical characteristics for single-current interchange circuits using optocouplers

V.32   A family of 2-wire duplex modems operating at data signalling rates of up to 9600 bit/s for use on the general switched telephone network and on leased telephone-type circuits

V.33   14 400 bits per second modem standardized for use
             on point-to-point 4-wire leased telephone-type circuits

V.35   Data transmission at 48 kilobits per second using
             60-108 kHz group band circuits

V.36   Modems for synchronous data transmission using
             60-108 kHz group band circuits

V.37   Synchronous data transmission at a data signalling
             rate higher than 72 kbit/s using 60-108 kHz grcup
             band circuits

V.40   Error indication with electromechanical equipment

V.41   Code-independent error-control system

V.42   Error-correcting procedures for DCEs using
             asynchronous-to-synchronous conversion

V.50   Standard limits for transmission quality of data
             transmission

V.51   Organisation of the maintenance of international
             telephone-type circuits used for data transmission

V.52   Characteristics of distortion and error-rate measuring
             apparatus for data transmission

V.53   Limits for the maintenance of telephone-type circuits
             used for data transmission

V.54   Loop test device for modems

V.55   Specification for an impulsive noise measuring
             instrument for telephone-type circuits

V.56   Comparative tests of modems for use over telephone-
             type circuits

V.57   Comprehensive data test set for high data signalling
             rates

V.100   Interconnection between public data networks (PDNs)
             and public switched telephone networks (PSTN)

V.110 Support of data terminal equipments (DTEs) with V-series type interfaces by an integrated services digital network (ISDN) (I.463)

V.120 Support by an ISDN of data terminal equipment with V-series type interfaces with provision for statistical multiplexing

V.230 General data communications interface layer 1 specification

X-Series Recommendations

X.1 International user classes of service in public data networks and Integrated Services Digital Networks (ISDNs)

X.2 International data transmission services and optional user facilities in public data networks and ISDNs

X.3 Packet assembly/disassembly facility (PAD) in a public data network

X.4 General structure of signals of International Alphabet No 5 code for character oriented data transmission over public data networks

X.10 Categories of access for Data Terminal Equipment (DTE) to public data transmission services

X.20 Interface between data terminal equipment (DTE) and data circuit-terminating equipment (DCE) for start-stop transmission services on public data networks

X.20bis Use on public data networks of data terminal equipment (DTE) which is designed for interfacing to asynchronous duplex V-series modems

X.21 Interface between data terminal equipment (DTE) and data circuit-terminating equipment (DCE) for synchronous operation on public data networks

X.21bis   Use on public data networks of data terminal equipment (DTE) which is designed for interfacing to synchronous V-series modems

X.22   Multiplex DTE/DCE interface for user classes 3-6

X.24   List of definitions for interchange circuits between data terminal equipment (DTE) and data circuit-terminating equipment (DCE) on public data networks

X.25   Interface between data terminal equipment (DTE) and data circuit-terminating equipment (DCE) for terminals operating in the packet mode and connected to public data networks by dedicated circuit

X.26   Electrical characteristics for unbalanced double-current interchange circuits for general use with integrated circuit equipment in the field of data communications (V.10)

X.27   Electrical characteristics for balanced double-current interchange circuits for general use with integrated circuit equipment in the field of data communications (V.11)

X.28   DTE/DCE interface for a start-stop mode data terminal equipment accessing the packet assembly/disassembly facility (PAD) in a public data network situated in the same country

X.29   Procedures for the exchange of control information and user data between a packet assembly/disassembly (PAD) facility and a packet mode DTE or another PAD

X.30   Support of X.21, X.21*bis* and X.20*bis* based data terminal equipments (DTEs) by an integrated services digital network (ISDN) (I.461)

X.31   Support of packet mode terminal equipment by an ISDN (I.462)

X.32   Interface between data terminal equipment (DTE) and data circuit-terminating equipment (DCE) for terminals operating in the packet mode and accessing a packet switched public data network through a public switched telephone network or an inte

X.40 Standardisation of frequency-shift modulated transmission systems for the provision of telegraph and data channels by frequency division of a group

X.50 Fundamental parameters of a multiplexing scheme for the international interface between synchronous data networks

X.50bis Fundamental parameters of a 48 kbit/s user data signalling rate transmission scheme for the international interface between synchronous data networks

X.51 Fundamental parameters of a multiplexing scheme for the international interface between synchronous data networks using 10-bit envelope structure

X.51bis Fundamental parameters of a 48 kbit/s user data signalling rate transmission scheme for the international interface between synchronous data networks using 10-bit envelope structure

X.52 Method of encoding anisochronous signals into a synchronous user bearer

X.53 Numbering of channels on international multiplex links at 64 kbit/s

X.54 Allocation of channels on international multiplex links at 64 kbit/s

X.55 Interface between synchronous data networks using a 6 + 2 envelope structure and single channel per carrier (SCPC) satellite channels

X.56 Interface between synchronous data networks using an 8 + 2 envelope structure and single channel per carrier (SCPC) satellite channels

X.57 Method of transmitting a single lower speed data channel on a 64 kbit/s data stream

X.58   Fundamental parameters of a multiplexing scheme for the international interface between synchronous non-switched data networks using no envelope structure

X.60   Common channel signalling for circuit switched data applications

X.61   Signalling System No 7 - data user part (Q.741)

X.70   Terminal and transit control signalling system for start-stop services on international circuits between anisochronous data networks

X.71   Decentralised terminal and transit control signalling system on international circuits between synchronous data networks

X.75   Packet-switched signalling system between public networks providing data transmission services

X.80   Interworking of interexchange signalling systems for circuit switched data services

X.81   Interworking between an ISDN circuit-switched and a circuit switched public data network (CSPDN)

X.82   Detailed arrangements for interworking between CSPDNs and PSPDNs based on Recommendation T.70

X.92   Hypothetical reference connections for public synchronous data networks

X.96   Call progress signals in public data networks

X.110   International routing principles and routing plan for public data networks

X.121   International numbering plan for public data networks

X.122   Numbering plan interworking between a packet switched public data network (PSPDN) and an integrated services digital network (ISDN) or public switched telephone network (PSTN) in the short term

X.209 Specification of basic encoding rules for abstract syntax notation one (ASN.1)

X.210 Open systems interconnection layer service conventions

X.211 Physical service definition of open systems interconnection for CCITT applications

X.212 Data link service definition for open systems interconnection for CCITT applications

X.213 Network service definition for open systems interconnection for CCITT applications

X.214 Transport service definition for open systems interconnection for CCITT applications

X.215 Session service definition for open systems interconnection for CCITT applications

X.216 Presentation service definition for open systems interconnection for CCITT applications

X.217 Association control service definition for open systems interconnection for CCITT applications

X.218 Reliable transfer: model and service definition

X.219 Remote operations: model, notation and service definition

X.220 Use of X.200-Series Protocols in CCITT Applications

X.223 Use of X.25 to provide the OSI connection-mode network service for CCITT applications

X.224 Transport protocol specification for Open Systems Interconnection for CCITT applications

X.225 Session protocol specification for Open Systems Interconnection for CCITT applications

X.226 Presentation protocol specification for Open Systems Interconnection for CCITT applications

X.227   Association control protocol specification for Open Systems Interconnection for CCITT applications

X.228   Reliable transfer: Protocol specification

X.229   Remote operations: Protocol specification

X.244   Procedure for the exchange of protocol identification during virtual call establishment on packet switched public data networks

X.290   OSI conformance testing methodology and framework for protocol Recommendations for CCITT applications

X.300   General principles for interworking between public networks and between public networks and other networks for the provision of data transmission services

X.301   Description of the general arrangements for call control within a subnetwork and between subnetworks for the provision of data transmission services

X.302   Description of the general arrangements for internal network utilities within a subnetwork and intermediate utilities between subnetworks for the provision of data transmission services

X.305   Functionalities of subnetworks relating to the support of the OSI connection-mode network service

X.320   General arrangements for interworking between integrated services digital networks (ISDNs) for the provision of data transmission services

X.321   General arrangements for interworking between circuit switched public data networks (CSPDNs) and integrated services digital networks (ISDNs) for the provision of data transmission services

X.322   General arrangements for interworking between packet switched public data networks (PSPDNs) and circuit switched public data networks (CSPDNs) for the provision of data transmission services

X.323   General arrangements for interworking between packet switched public data networks (PSPDNs)

X.324   General arrangements for interworking between packet switched public data networks (PSPDNs) and mobile systems for the provision of data transmission services

X.325   General arrangements for interworking between packet switched public data networks (PSPDNs) and integrated services digital networks (ISDNs) for the provision of data transmissions services (I.540)

X.326   General arrangements for interworking between packet switched public data networks (PSPDNs) and common channel signalling network (CCSN)

X.327   General arrangements for interworking between packet switched public data networks (PSPDNs) and private data networks for the provision of data transmission services

X.350   General requirements to be met for data transmission in international public mobile satellite systems

X.351   Special requirements to be met for packet assembly/disassembly facilities (PADs) located at or in association with coast earth stations in the public mobile satellite service

X.352   Interworking between public packet switched data networks and public maritime mobile satellite data transmission systems

X.353   Routing principles for interconnecting public maritime mobile satellite data transmission systems with public data networks

X.370   Arrangements for the transfer of internetwork management information

X.400   Message handling system and service overview

X.402   Message handling systems: Overall architecture

Z-Series Recommendations

1.3   1992 CCITT RECOMMENDATIONS (draft)

F-Series Recommendations

F.435   Message Handling: EDI messaging service

G-Series Recommendations

G.708   Network node interface for the synchronous digital hierarchy

G.764   Voice packetization: packetized voice protocols

I-Series Recommendations

I.122   (Frame relay)

X-Series Recommendations

X.435   Message Handling System: EDI messaging system

X.701   Systems management overview for CCITT applications

X.710   Common Management Information Service definition for CCITT applications

X.711   Common Management Information Protocol specification for CCITT applications

X.721   Definition of management information for CCITT applications

X.722   Guidelines for the definition of managed objects for CCITT applications

X.730   Object management function for CCITT applications

1.4   ISO STANDARDS

ISO 17   Guide to the use of preferred numbers

ISO 31   Quantities, units and symbols

ISO 261   ISO Metric Screw Threads - General plan

ISO 639   Symbols for languages, geographical areas and
                    authorities

ISO 646   Information processing - ISO 7-bit coded character set
                    for information interchange

ISO 962   Information processing - Implementation of the ISO
                    7-bit coded character set and its 7-bit and 8-bit
                    extensions on 9-track 12.7 mm (0.5 in) magnetic tape

ISO 963   Rules for the derivation of 4-bit coded character sets

ISO 1155   Information processing - Use of longitudinal parity to
                    detect errors in information messages

ISO 1177   Information processing - Character structure for start/
                    stop and synchronous character oriented transmission

ISO 1745   Information processing - Basic mode control
                    procedures for data communication systems

ISO 2022   Information processing - ISO 7-bit and 8-bit coded
                    character sets - code extension techniques

ISO 2110   Data communications - 25 pin DTE/DCE interface
                    connector and pin assignments
                    PDAM 1: Interface connector and contact
                             assignments for a DTE/DCE interface for
                             data signalling rates above 20 Kbit/s

ISO 2111   Data communications - Basic mode control procedures
                    - code independent information transfer

ISO 2375   Data processing - Procedures for the registration of
                    escape sequences

ISO 2382   Information processing - Vocabulary
                  Part 1:   Fundamental terms
                  Part 9:   Data communication
                  Part 18:   Distributed data processing
                  Part 25:   Local area networks
                  Part 26:   OSI architecture

ISO 2530   Keyboard for international information processing
                  interchange using the ISO 7-bit coded character set -
                  alphanumeric area

ISO 2593   Information technology - 34-pole DTE/DCE interface
                  connector and contact number assignments
                  WDAM x: Adaptor for attachment of DTEs using
                              34-pole connector to DCEs

ISO 2628   Complements to the basic mode control procedures -
                  recovery, abort and interrupt multiple station selection

ISO 2629   Basic mode control procedures - conversational
                  information message transfer

ISO 2955   Information processing - Representation of SI and
                  other units in systems with limited character sets

ISO 3166   Codes for the representation of names of countries

ISO 3307   Information interchange - Representation of time of the
                  day

ISO 3309   Information processing systems - Data communication
                  - High-level data link control procedures - frame
                  structure
                  PDAM 2: Extended transparency options for
                              start/stop transmission

ISO 3511   Industrial process measurement control functions and
                  instrumentation - Symbolic representation
                  Part 4:   Basic symbols for process computer,
                              interface and shared display/control
                              functions

ISO 4031   Information interchange - Representation of local time
                  differentials

ISO 4217   Codes for the representation of currencies and funds

ISO 4335   Information processing systems - Data communication
- High-level data link control elements of procedures
AM2:   Enhancement of the XID function utility
PDAM 4: Flow control unnumbered information (FUI)
frame
PDAM 5: Multi-selective reject function

ISO 4873   Information processing - ISO 8-bit code for information
interchange - structure and rules for implementation

ISO 4902   Information technology - 37-pole DTE/DCE interface
connector and contact number assignments

ISO 4903   Data communications - 15-pin DTE/DCE interface
connector and pin assignments

ISO 5218   Information interchange - Representation of human
sexes

ISO 6429   Information processing - Control functions for 7-bit and
8-bit coded character sets

ISO 6936   Information processing - Conversion between the
coded character sets of ISO 646 and ISO 6937-2 and
CCITT International Telegraph Alphabet No 2 (ITA 2)

ISO 6937   Information processing - Coded character sets for text
communication
Part 1:   General introduction
Part 2:   Latin alphabetic and non-alphabetic graphic
characters
Part 3:   Control functions for page image format
Part 4:   Control functions for formatted and
formattable text
Part 5:   Scientific and technical graphic characters
Part 6:   Publishing and box drawing graphic
characters
Part 7:   Greek graphic characters
Part 8:   Cyrillic graphic characters

DP 6950   Point-to-point full duplex interface

PDTR 7352 Information processing - Guidelines for the organization and representation of data elements for data interchange
Part 1: Basis for the interchange of data

ISO 7372 Trade Data Interchange - Trade data elements directory
Part 1: Data elements in international maritime, road and multi-modal transport, customs and invoice applications

TR 7477 Data communications - General arrangements for DTE to DTE physical connection using V.24 and X.24 interchange circuits

ISO 7478 Information processing - Multilink procedures

ISO 7480 Information processing - Start/Stop transmission signal quality at the DTE/DCE interface

CD 7480 Information processing - Start/Stop transmission signal quality at the DTE/DCE interface

ISO 7498 Information processing systems - Open Systems Interconnection - Open Systems Interconnection Basic Reference Model
Part 1: Basic Reference Model
AM1: Connectionless-mode transmission
PDAM 2: Multi-peer data transmission
WDAMx: General Aspects
Part 2: Security architecture
Part 3: Naming and addressing
Part 4: Management framework

ISO 7776 Information processing systems - Data communication - High-level data link control procedures - Description of the X.25 LAPB-compatible DTE data link procedures
PDAM 1: PICS proforma

ISO 7809 Information processing systems - Data communication - High-level data link control procedures - Classes of procedures

PDAM 4: Lists of standard data link layer protocols that utilize HDLC classes of procedure

PDAM 5: Connectionless classes of procedures

PDAM 6: Extended transparency options for start/stop transmission

PDAM 7: Multi-selective reject function

PDAM 9: Seven-bit transparency option for start/stop transmission

ISO 7942 Information processing systems - Computer graphics - Graphical Kernel System (GKS) functional description

DAM 1: Audit trail metafile and encoding

ISO 8072 Information processing systems - Open Systems Inter-connection - Transport Service definition

AM 1: Connectionless-mode transmission

ISO 8073 Information processing systems - Open Systems Inter-connection - Connection-Oriented Transport Protocol specification

AM 1: Addendum to provide Network Connection Management Sub-protocol

AM2: Addendum to provide Connection-Oriented Transport Protocol over Connectionless Network Service

PDAM3: PICS proforma

PDAM4: Protocol enhancements

PDAMx: Cryptographic data protection

ISO 8208 Information technology - X.25 packet level protocol for data terminal equipment

DAM 1: Alternative logical channel identifier assignment

DAM 2: Extensions for private switched use

PDAM 3: Conformance requirements

PDAM 4: PICS proforma

ISO 8211 Information processing - Specification of a data descriptive file for information interchange

DIS 8227 Information processing - Data Encipherment - Specification of algorithm DEA1

ISO 8326   Information processing systems - Open Systems Inter-
connection - Basic Connection-Oriented Session
Service Definition
AM 1:   Session symmetric synchronization for the
          session service
DAM 2:   Incorporation of unlimited user data
AM3:   Connectionless-mode Session service
PDAM 4: Incorporation of additional synchronization
          functionality

ISO 8327   Information processing systems - Open Systems Inter-
connection - Basic Connection-Oriented Session
Protocol Specification
AM 1:   Session symmetric synchronization for the
          session protocol
PDAM 3: Incorporation of additional synchronization
          functionality
Part 2: Protocol Implementation Conformance
          Statement

ISO 8348   Information processing systems - Data communication
- Network service definition
AM 1:   Connectionless-mode transmission
AM 2:   Network Layer addressing
PDAM 3: Additional features of the network service
PDAM 4: Removal of the preferred decimal encoding
          of the NSAP address

ISO 8372   Information processing - Modes of operation for a
64-bit block cipher algorithm
Part 1: Dimensional, physical and magnetic
          characteristics
Part 2: Track format A
Part 3: Track format B

ISO 8471   Information processing - High-level data link control
balanced classes of procedures - Data-link layer
address resolution/negotiation in switched
environments

DP 8472   Data communications - X.25 (1980) Network
Convergence Protocol

ISO 8473   Information processing - Protocol for providing the connectionless-mode Network Service
                  AM 3:   Provision of the underlying service assumed by ISO 8473 over subnetworks which provide the OSI data link service
                  AM x: PICS proforma
                  AM y: Provision of the underlying service assumed by ISO 8473 over ISDN circuit-switched B-channels

ISO 8480   Information processing - DTE/DCE interface back-up control operation using the 25-pole connector

ISO 8481   Data communications - DTE to DTE physical connection using X.24 interchange circuits with DTE provided timing

ISO 8482   Information processing - Twisted pair multipoint interconnections

TR 8509   Information processing systems - Open Systems Interconnection - Service conventions

ISO 8571   Information processing systems - Open Systems Interconnection - File Transfer, Access and Management
                  Part 1:   General Description
                             DAM 1:   Filestore Management
                             PDAM 2:   Overlapped access
                             WDAM 3: Service enhancement
                  Part 2:   Virtual filestore definition
                             DAM 1:   Filestore management
                             PDAM 2:   Overlapped access
                             WDAM 3: Service enhancement
                  Part 3:   File Service Definition
                             DAM 1:   Filestore management
                             PDAM 2:   Overlapped access
                             WDAM 3: Service enhancement
                  Part 4:   File Protocol Specification
                             DAM 1:   Filestore management
                             PDAM 2:   Overlapped access
                             WDAM 3: Service enhancement

Part 5:   Protocol Implementation Conformance
          Statement proforma
          PDAM 1: Filestore management
          PDAM 2: Overlapped access

ISO 8602   Information processing systems - Open Systems Inter-
               connection - Protocol for providing the
               Connectionless-Mode Transport Service utilizing the
               Connectionless-Mode Network Service or the
               Connection-Oriented Network Service

ISO 8613   Information processing systems - Text and office
               systems - Office Document Architecture (ODA) and
               interchange format
               Part 1:   Introduction and general principles
                         DAM 1:   Application profile proforma and
                                  notation
                         DAM 2:   Conformance testing
                                  methodology
                         DAM 3:   Alternate representation
                         DAM 4:   Security
                         DAM 5:   Streams
                         DAM 6:   Styles extension
               Part 2:   Document structures
               Part 4:   Document Profile
                         PDAM 1: Additive extensions for filing and
                                  retrieval attributes
                         PDAM 2: Document application profile
                                  proforma and notation
               Part 5:   Office Document Interchange Format (ODIF)
               Part 6:   Character content architectures
               Part 7:   Raster graphics content architectures
                         DAM 1:   Tiled raster graphics content
                                  architectures
                         WDAM x: Formal specification of raster
                                  graphics content architectures
               Part 8:   Geometric graphics content architectures
               Part 9:   Audio content architectures
               Part 10: Formal specifications
                         DAM 1:   Formal specification of the
                                  document profile

DAM 2:   Formal specification of the raster graphics content architectures

ISO 8632   Information processing systems - Computer graphics - Metafile for the storage and transfer of picture description information (CGM)
Part 1:   Functional specification
PDAM 1: Extended metafile (2D)
PDAM 2: 3D static picture capture metafile
Part 2:   Character Encoding
DAM 1:   Extended metafile (2D)
Part 3:   Binary Encoding
PDAM 1: Extended metafile (2D)
Part 4:   Clear Text Encoding
PDAM 1: Extended metafile (2D)

ISO 8648   Information processing systems - Data communication - Internal organisation of the Network Layer

ISO 8649   Information processing systems - Open Systems Interconnection - Service Definition for the Association Control Service Element
AM 1:   Authentication during association establishment
AD 2:   Connectionless-mode ACSE service
DAM 3:   A-CONTEXT Management Service

ISO 8650   Information processing systems - Open Systems Interconnection - Protocol specification for the Association Control Service Element
AM 1:   Authentication during association establishment
PDAM 2: Protocol Implementation Conformance Statement (PICS) proforma
PDAM 3: Application entity titles
Part 2:   Protocol Implementation Conformance Statement (PICS) proforma

ISO 8651   Information technology - Graphical Kernel System (GKS) language bindings
Part 1:   FORTRAN
Part 2:   Pascal

Part 3:   Ada
Part 4:   C

ISO 8731   Banking - Approved algorithms for message
authentication
Part 1:   DEA 1
Part 2:   Message authentication algorithm
Part 3:   Programmable calculator authenticator

ISO 8732   Banking - Key management for message
authentication

ISO 8802   Information processing - Local Area Networks
Part 1:   General introduction
Section E: System load protocol
Part 2:   Logical Link Control
DAM 1:   Flow control techniques for
multi-segment networks
DAM 2:   Acknowledged
connectionless-mode service and
protocol, Type 3 operation
PDAM 3:   PICS proforma
PDAM 4:   Editorial changes and technical
corrections to ISO 8802-2
Part 3:   Carrier Sense Multiple Access with Collision
Detection (CSMA/CD) access method and
Physical Layer specifications
DAM 1:   Medium Attachment Unit and
baseband medium specification
for Type 10base2
DAM2:   Repeater set and repeater unit
specification for use with
10Base5 and 10Base2 networks
DAM 3:   Broadband Medium Attachment
Unit and broadband medium
specifications for type 10Broad36
DAM 4:   Physical signalling, medium
attachment and baseband
medium specifications, StarLAN,
type 1Base5
DAM 5:   Medium attachment unit and
baseband medium attachment

specification for a vendor
independent fibre

PDAM 6: Summary of IEEE 802.3 first
maintenance ballot

PDAM 7: LAN layer management

PDAM 9: Physical medium, medium
attachment and baseband
medium specifications, type
10BaseT

Part 4: Token-passing bus access method and
Physical Layer specifications

Part 5: Token ring access method and Physical
Layer specifications

PDAM 1: 4 and 16 Mbit/s specification for
Token Ring Networks

PDAM 2: Token ring MAC sublayer
enhancement

PDAM 3: Management entity specification

PDAM 4: MAC sublayer bridging - source
routing

PDAM 5: PICS proforma

PDAM x: Multi-ring networks

Part 7: Slotted ring access method and Physical
Layer specifications

DIS 8805   Information processing - Graphical kernel system for
three dimensions (GKS 3-D) functional description
PDAM 1: Name set addendum

DIS 8806   Information technology - Graphical Kernel System for
three dimensions (GKS-3D) language bindings
Part 1:   FORTRAN
Part 4:   C

ISO 8807   Information processing systems - Open Systems Interconnection - LOTOS - a formal description technique
based on the temporal ordering of observational
behaviour
PDAM 1: G-LOTOS

ISO 8822 Information processing systems - Open Systems Inter-
connection - Connection oriented presentation service
definition
AM 1: Connectionless-mode Presentation service
PDAM 2: Support of session symmetric
synchronization service
PDAM 3: Specification of registration of abstract
syntaxes
PDAM 5: To deliver additional Session
synchronization functionality to the
Presentation Service user
WDAM y: Use of session unlimited user data

ISO 8823 Information technology - Open Systems Inter-
connection - Connection oriented Presentation protocol
definition
PDAM 2: Support of session symmetric
synchronization service
PDAM 3: Specification of registration of abstract
syntaxes
WDAM 4: Unlimited user data
PDAM 5: To deliver additional Session
synchronization functionality to the
Presentation Service user
Part 2: Protocol Implementation Conformance
Statement proforma (PICS)

ISO 8824 Information technology - Open Systems Inter-
connection - Specification of Abstract Syntax Notation
One (ASN.1)
Part 1: Basic ASN.1
Part 2: Information object classes
Part 3: Constraint specification
Part 4: Parameterisation

ISO 8825 Information technology - Open Systems Inter-
connection - Specification of encoding rules for
Abstract Syntax Notation One (ASN.1)
Part 1: Basic Encoding Rules
Part 2: Packed Encoding Rules
Part 3: Distinguished Encoding Rules

ISO 8831   Information processing systems - Open Systems Inter-
                 connection - Job Transfer and Manipulation concepts
                 and services

ISO 8832   Information processing systems - Open Systems Inter-
                 connection - Specification of the Basic Class Protocol
                 for Job Transfer and Manipulation
                 AM 1:   Extension to specification of the full protocol

ISO 8859   Information Processing - Registration of graphics
                 character subrepertoires - 8-bit single byte coded
                 graphic character sets
                 Part 1:   Latin alphabet No 1
                 Part 2:   Latin alphabet No 2
                 Part 3:   Latin alphabet No 3
                 Part 4:   Latin alphabet No 4
                 Part 5:   Latin/Cyrillic alphabet
                 Part 6:   Latin/Arabic alphabet
                 Part 7:   Latin/Greek alphabet
                 Part 8:   Latin/Hebrew alphabet
                 Part 9:   Latin alphabet No 5

ISO 8867   Industrial asynchronous data link and physical layer
                 Part 1:   Physical interconnection and two-way
                             alternate communication

ISO 8877   Information processing - Interface connector and
                 contact assignments for ISDN basic access interface
                 located at reference points S and T
                 DAM 1:   TE connecting cord

ISO 8878   Information processing - Use of X.25 to provide the
                 OSI connection-mode network service
                 DAM 1:   Priority
                 AM 2:   Use of an X.25 PVC to provide the OSI
                            CONS
                 DAM 3:   Conformance
                 PDAM 4:   Protocol Implementation Conformance
                            Statement

ISO 8879   Information processing - Standard Generalised Markup
                 Language (SGML)

ISO 8880   Information processing systems - Open Systems Inter-
                 connection - Protocol combinations to provide and
                 support the OSI Network Service
                 Part 1:   General principles
                 Part 2:   Provision and support of the
                             connection-mode network service
                             PDAM 1: Addition of the ISDN environment
                                      when a packet handling function
                                      is present
                             PDAM 2: Addition of the PSTN and CSDN
                                      environments
                 Part 3:   Provision and support of the
                             connectionless-mode Network Service
                 Part 4:   Interconnection of OSI network
                             environments

ISO 8881   Information processing - Use of the X.25 packet level
                 protocol in local area networks
                 Part 1:   Use with Logical Link Control Type 1
                             procedures
                 Part 2:   Use with Logical Link Control Type 2
                             procedures

DP 8882   Information processing - X.25 DTE Conformance
                 Testing
                 Part 1:   General principles
                 Part 2:   Data Link Layer conformance test suite
                 Part 3:   Packet level conformance test suite

DIS 8884   Information processing - Keyboards for multiple latin
                 alphabet languages - layout and operation using four
                 levels

ISO 8885   Information processing - High-level data link control
                 procedures - General purpose XID frame information
                 field content and format
                 PDAM 3: Definition of a private parameter data link
                          layer subfield
                 PDAM 4: Extended transparency options for
                          start/stop transmission
                 PDAM 5: Multi-selective reject function

PDAM 6: Seven-bit transparency option for Start/Stop transmission

PDAM 7: FCS negotiation using the parameter negotation data link layer subfield

DIS 8886   Information processing - Data-Link service definition for Open Systems Interconnection

ISO 8907   Information processing - Network database language NDL

TR 9007   Information processing - Concepts and terminology for the conceptual schema and the information base

ISO 9036   Information processing - Arabic 7-bit coded character set for information interchange

ISO 9040   Information technology - Open Systems Interconnection - Virtual terminal basic class service
Part 1:   Specification
            DAM 2:   Additional functional units
Part 2:   Protocol Implementation Conformance Statement (PICS) proforma

ISO 9066   Information processing - Reliable transfer
Part 1:   Model and service definition
Part 2:   Protocol specification

ISO 9067   Information processing - Automatic fault isolation procedures using test loops

DP 9068   Information processing - Provision of the connectionless Network Service using ISO 8208

ISO 9069   Information processing - SGML Document Interchange Format (SDIF)

ISO 9070   Information processing - SGML Support Facilities - registration procedures for public text owner identifiers

ISO 9072   Information processing - Remote operations
Part 1:   Model, notation and service definition
Part 2:   Protocol specification

DIS 9074   Information processing systems - Open Systems Interconnection - Estelle, a formal description technique based on an extended state transition model
PDAM 1:   Estelle Tutorial

ISO 9075   Information processing - Database Language SQL with integrity enhancement

CD 9075   Information processing - Database language SQL2

DIS 9126   Information technology - Software product evaluation - Quality characteristics and guidelines for their use

ISO 9127   Information processing - User documentation and cover information for consumer software packages

ISO 9160   Information processing - Physical layer interoperability requirements

ISO 9281   Coded character sets for pictorial graphics
Part 1:   Identification mechanism for picture coding methods
Part 2:   Procedure for registration

ISO 9282   Information processing - Coded representation of pictures
Part 1:   Encoding principles for picture representation in a 7-bit or 8-bit environment

TR 9294   Information technology - Guidelines for the management of software documentation

DP 9307   DEA2 - a Public Key algorithm

ISO 9314   Information processing - Fibre Distributed Data Interface (FDDI)
Part 1:   Token Ring Physical Layer protocol (PHY)
Part 2:   Token Ring Media Access Control (MAC)
Part 3:   Physical Layer Medium Dependent (PMD)
Part 5:   Hybrid Ring Control (FDDI-II)

ISO 9496   Information Processing Systems - Programming Languages - CCITT high level language (CHILL)

DIS 9506   Industrial Automation Systems - Systems Integration and Communications - Manufacturing message specification
Part 1:   Service definition
Part 2:   Protocol specification
Part 3:   Robot controller message specification
Part 4:   Numerical controller message specification
Part 5:   Programmable controller message specification
Part 6:   Process industries message specification
Part 7:   Production management message specification

DIS 9541   Information processing - Font and character information interchange
Part 1:   Architecture
Part 2:   Interchange format
Part 3:   Glyph shape representations
Part 4:   Character collections
Part 5:   Font attributes and character model
Part 6:   Font and character attribute subsets and applications
Part 7:   Font interchange format

ISO 9542   Information processing - End system to intermediate system routeing exchange protocol for use in conjunction with the protocol for providing the connectionless-mode Network Service (ISO 8473)
PDAM 1: Dynamic discovery of OSI NSAP addresses by end systems

ISO 9543   Information processing - Synchronous transmission signal quality at DTE/DCE interfaces

ISO 9545   Information technology - Open Systems Interconnection - Application Layer structure
PDAM 1: Extended Application Layer structure

ISO 9548   Information processing systems - Open Systems Interconnection - Connectionless session protocol specification
Part 2:   Protocol Implementation Conformance Statement proforma (PICS)

DIS 9549   Information technology - Galvanic isolation of balanced interchange circuits

TR 9571   Information technology - Open Systems Interconnection - LOTOS description of the session service

TR 9572   Information technology - Open Systems Interconnection - LOTOS description of the session protocol

TR 9573   Information processing - SGML support facilities - Techniques for using SGML
Part 13:   Public entity sets for mathematics and science

ISO 9574   Information technology - Telecommunications and information exchange between systems - Provision of the OSI connection-mode network service by packet mode terminal equipment connected to an integrated services digital network (ISDN)
PDAM 1:   Operation over an ISDN circuit-switched channel connecting directly to the remote terminal

TR 9575   Information technology - Telecommunications and information exchange between systems - OSI routeing framework

ISO 9576   Information processing systems - Open Systems Interconnection - Connectionless Presentation protocol
Part 1:   Specification
Part 2:   Protocol Implementation Conformance Statement proforma

TR 9577   Information technology - Telecommunications and information exchange between systems - Protocol identification in the Network Layer

TR 9578   Information technology - Communication interface connectors used in local area networks

ISO 9579   Information technology - Remote database access
Part 1:   Generic model, service and protocol
Part 2:   SQL specialization

ISO 9592   Information processing systems - Computer graphics - Programmer's Hierarchical Interactive Graphics System (PHIGS)
Part 1:   Functional description
            AM 1:   PHIGS Plus support
Part 2:   Archive file format
            AM 2:   PHIGS Plus support
Part 3:   Clear-text encoding of archive file
            AM 1:   PHIGS Plus support
Part 4:   PHIGS Plus

DIS 9593   Information technology - Programmer's Hierarchical Interactive Graphics System (PHIGS) language bindings
Part 1:   FORTRAN binding
Part 2:   Pascal binding
Part 3:   Ada
Part 4:   C

ISO 9594   Information technology - Open Systems Interconnection - The Directory
Part 1:   Overview of concepts, models and services
            PDAM 1: Replication, schema and access
                     control
Part 2:   Models
            PDAM 1: Access control
            PDAM 2: Schema extensions
            PDAM 3: Replication
Part 3:   Abstract service definition
            PDAM 1: Access control
            PDAM 2: Replication, schema and
                     enhanced search

Part 4: Procedures for distributed operation
PDAM 1: Access control
PDAM 2: Replication, schema and
enhanced search
Part 5: Protocol specifications
PDAM 1: Replication
Part 6: Selected attribute types
PDAM 1: Schema extensions
Part 7: Selected object classes
PDAM 1: Schema extensions
Part 8: Authentication Framework
PDAM 1: Access control
Part 9: Replication
Part 10: Directory PICS proforma

ISO 9595 Information technology - Open Systems Inter-connection - Common management information service definition
DAM 1: CancelGet service
DAM 2: Add/Remove service
PDAM 3: Support for allomorphism
PDAM 4: Access control

ISO 9596 Information technology - Open Systems Inter-connection - Common management information protocol specification
Part 1: Specification
DAM 1: CancelGet protocol
DAM 2: Add/Remove protocol
PCDAM 4:Support for allomorphism
Part 2: Protocol Implementation Conformance
Statement (PICS) proforma

DP 9636 Information processing systems - Computer graphics - Computer Graphics Interface (CGI) techniques for dialogues with graphical devices
Part 1: Overview
Part 2: Control, negotiation and errors
Part 3: Output and attributes
Part 4: Segmentation
Part 5: Input and echoing
Part 6: Raster

DP 9637   Computer Graphics Interface (CGI) - Interface techniques for dialogues with graphical devices - CGI data encoding
Part 1:   Character encoding
Part 2:   Binary encoding
Part 3:   Clear text encoding

DP 9638   Computer Graphics Interface (CGI) - Interface techniques for dialogues with graphical devices - CGI library language bindings
Part 1:   FORTRAN
Part 2:   Pascal
Part 3:   Ada
Part 4:   C

ISO 9646   Information technology - Open Systems Interconnection - Conformance testing methodology and framework
Part 1:   General concepts
Part 2:   Abstract test suite specification
Part 3:   The Tree and Tabular Combined Notation (TTCN)
Part 4:   Test realization
Part 5:   Requirements on test laboratories and clients for the conformance assessment process
Part 6:   Protocol profile test specification

ISO 9735   Electronic data interchange for administration, commerce and transport (EDIFACT) - Application level syntax rules

DP 9788   Information processing - Data cryptographic techniques - Peer entity authentication mechanisms using an N-bit secret-key algorithm

PDTR 9789   Information processing - Guidelines for the organization and representation of data elements for data interchange - coding methods and principles

DP 9796   Information processing - Data cryptographic techniques - Digital signatures scheme with shadow using a public-key system

DIS 9797   Information processing - Data integrity mechanism using a cryptographic check function using an n-bit algorithm with truncation

DP 9798   Information processing - Data cryptographic techniques - Peer entity authentication mechanism using an n-bit secret-key algorithm

DP 9799   Information processing - Data cryptographic techniques - Peer entity authentication mechanism using a public-key algorithm with a two-way handshake

ISO 9804   Information technology - Open Systems Interconnection - Service definition for the Commitment, Concurrency and Recovery service element
PDAM 1: Enhancements
PDAM 2: Session mapping changes

ISO 9805   Information technology - Open Systems Interconnection - Protocol specification for the Commitment, Concurrency and Recovery service element
PDAM 1: Enhancements
PDAM 2: Session mapping changes
Part 2:   Protocol Implementation Conformance Statement proforma

DIS 9834   Information technology - Open Systems Interconnection - Procedures for specific OSI Registration Authorities
Part 1:   General procedures
Part 2:   Registration procedures for OSI document types
Part 3:   Registration of object identifier component values for joint ISO-CCITT use
Part 4:   Register of VT Profiles
Part 5:   Register of VT Control Object definitions
Part 6:   Registration of AP Titles and AE Titles

ISO 9945   Information technology - Portable operating system interface for computer environments (POSIX)
Part 1:   System Application Program Interface (API)

CD 9955   Methodology and guidelines for the development of Application protocols for banking information interchange

TR 9973   Information processing - Procedures for registration of graphical items

DIS 9979   Information processing - Data cryptographic techniques - Procedures for the registration of cryptographic algorithms

DP 9995   Information processing - Keyboard layouts for text and office systems

TR 10000   Information technology - Framework and taxonomy of International Standardized Profiles
Part 1:   Framework
Part 2:   Taxonomy

ISO 10021   Information technology - Text communication - Message-Oriented Text Interchange Systems (MOTIS)
WDAM x: MTS routing
WDAM y: Inlog and Outlog in message store
Part 1:   System and service overview
Part 2:   Overall architecture
Part 3:   Abstract service definition conventions
Part 4:   Message Transfer System: abstract service definition and procedures
Part 5:   Message store: abstract service definition
Part 6:   Protocol specifications
Part 7:   Interpersonal Messaging System

DIS 10022   Information processing systems - Open Systems Interconnection - Physical service definition

DTR 10023   Information processing systems - Open Systems Interconnection - Formal description of ISO 8072 in LOTOS

PDTR 10024   Information processing systems - Open Systems Interconnection - Formal description of the connection-oriented Transport Protocol in LOTOS

DP 10025   Information processing systems - Open Systems Interconnection - Transport conformance testing for the

connection-oriented Transport Protocol operating over the connection-oriented Network Service
Part 1:   General principles
Part 2:   Test suite structure and test purposes

DIS 10026   Information technology - Open Systems Inter-connection - Distributed transaction processing
Part 1:   Model
Part 2:   Service Definition
            AM 1:   Commit optimizations
Part 3:   Protocol Specification
Part 4:   Protocol Implementation Conformance Statement (PICS) proforma
Part 5:   Application context proforma
Part 6:   Unstructured data transfer

ISO 10027   Information technology - Information Resource Dictionary System (IRDS) framework

DP 10028   Information processing - Definition of the relaying functions of a Network Layer intermediate system
Part 1:   Connection-mode Network Service
Part 2:   Connectionless Network Service

TR 10029   Information technology - Telecommunications and information exchange between systems - Operation of an X.25 interworking unit

ISO 10030   Information technology - Telecommunications and information exchange between systems - End system to intermediate system routeing exchange protocol for use in conjunction with ISO 8878
PDAM 1:   Dynamic discovery of OSI NSAP addresses by end-systems
PDAM 3:   Specification of IS-SNARE interactions
Part 2:   PICS proforma

ISO 10031   Information technology - Distributed-office-applications Model
Part 1:   General Model
Part 2:   Referenced data transfer

CD 10032   Information technology - Reference model of data management

ISO 10035   Information processing systems - Open Systems Interconnection - Connectionless ACSE protocol specification

DP 10036   Information processing - Procedure for registration of glyph and glyph collection identifiers

DTR 10037   Information processing - SGML and text-entry systems - Guidelines for SGML syntax-directed editing systems

DIS 10038   Information processing systems - Local area networks - MAC sublayer interconnection (MAC bridging)
PDAM 1:   Specification of management information for CMIP
PDAM 2:   Source routing supplement

DIS 10039   Information technology - Telecommunications and information exchange between systems - Medium access control service definition

DIS 10040   Information technology - Open Systems Interconnection - Systems management overview

DP 10070   Information processing systems - Open Systems Interconnection - Upper Layer Conformance Testing
Part 1:   FTAM test structure and purpose

DP 10116   Information processing - Modes of operation for an n-bit block cipher algorithm

DP 10118   Information processing - Data cryptographic techniques - Hash functions for digital signatures

DP 10148   Information processing systems - Open Systems Interconnection - Basic Remote Procedure Call (RPC) using OSI Remote Operations

DIS 10160   Information and documentation - Open Systems Interconnection - Application service for information systems - Interlibrary loan application service definition

DIS 10161 Information and documentation - Open Systems Inter-connection - Application protocol for information systems - Interlibrary loan application protocol specification

DIS 10162 Information and documentation - Open Systems Inter-connection - Application service for information systems - Bibliographic search, retrieve and update service definition

DIS 10163 Information and documentation - Open Systems Inter-connection - Application protocol for information systems - Bibliographic search, retrieve and update protocol specification

DIS 10164 Information processing systems - Open Systems Inter-connection - Systems management
Part 1: Object management function
Part 2: State management function
Part 3: Attributes for representing relationships
Part 4: Alarm reporting function
Part 5: Event report management function
Part 6: Log control function
Part 7: Security alarm reporting function
Part 8: Security audit trail function
Part 9: Objects and attributes for access control
Part 10: Accounting meter function
Part 11: Workload monitoring function
Part 12: Test management function
Part 13: Summarization function
Part cdt: Confidence and diagnostic testing function
Part sdm: Software distribution management function
Part tm: Time management function
Part pm: Performance management
Part cdtc: Confidence and diagnostic test classes

DIS 10165 Information technology - Open Systems Inter-connection - Structure of management information
Part 1: Management information model
Part 2: Definition of management information
Part 4: Guidelines for the definition of managed objects

Part 5:   Generic management information
Part 6:   Requirements and guidelines for
            conformance statement proformas
            associated with management information
Part 7:   Management information register and
            registration procedures

ISO 10166   Information technology - Document filing and retrieval
                (DFR)
                Part 1:   Abstract service definition and procedures
                Part 2:   Protocol specification

DTR 10167   Information technology - Guidelines for the application
                of Estelle, LOTOS and SDL

DP 10168   Information technology - Open Systems Inter-
                connection - Conformance test suite for the Session
                Protocol
                Part 1:   Test suite structure and test purposes
                Part 4:   Test management protocol specification

DIS 10169   Information technology - Open Systems Inter-
                connection - Conformance test suite for the ACSE
                Protocol
                Part 1:   Test suite structure and test purposes

DIS 10170   Information technology - Open Systems Inter-
                connection - Conformance test suite for the FTAM
                Protocol
                Part 1:   Test suite structure and test purposes

TR 10171   Information processing - List of standard data link
                protocols that utilise high-level data link control (HDLC)
                classes of procedures
                PDAM 1:   Registration of XID format identifiers and
                          private parameter set identifiers

PDTR 10172 Information processing - Network/Transport protocol
                interworking specification

DP 10173   Information processing - Integrated Services Digital
                Network (ISDN) primary access connector at reference
                points S and T

PDTR 10174 Logical Link Control (Type 2) test purposes

DP 10175 Information processing systems - Text and office systems - Document printing application
Part 1: Abstract service definition and procedures
Part 2: Protocol specification

DIS 10177 Information technology - Intermediate system support of the OSI connection-mode Network service using ISO/IEC 8208 in accordance with ISO/IEC 10028

PDTR 10178 Information technology - Telecommunications and information exchange between systems - The structure and coding of Link Service Access Point addresses in Local Area Networks

DP 10179 DSSSL - Document style semantics and specification language

DP 10180 Standard Page Description Language

CD 10181 Information processing systems - Open Systems Interconnection - Security frameworks for open systems
Part 1: Overview
Part 2: Authentication framework
Part 3: Access control framework
Part 4: Non-repudiation framework
Part 5: Confidentiality framework
Part 6: Integrity framework
Part 7: Audit trail framework

PDTR 10183 Information processing - Office document architecture (ODA) and interchange format - implementation testing methodology
Part 1: Framework
Part 2: Abstract test cases

CD 10184 Information processing systems - Open Systems Interconnection - Terminal management - model

DIS 10222 Information processing - Enhanced Small Device Interface

DIS 10288   Information processing - Enhanced small computer
system interface (SCSI-2)

DIS 10367   Information technology - 8-bit code for information
interchange

DIS 10538   Information technology - Control functions for text
communication

DP 10588   Information technology - Telecommunications and
information exchange between systems - Use of X.25
PLP in conjunction with X.21/X.21bis to provide the OSI
Connection-Oriented Network Service

DIS 10589   Information technology - Telecommunications and
information exchange between systems - Intermediate
system intra-domain routing exchange protocol for use
in conjunction with the protocol for providing the
connectionless-mode network service (ISO 8473)

DISP 10607   Information technology - International Standardized
Profiles AFTnn - File Transfer, Access and
Management
Part 1:   Specification of ACSE, Presentation and
Session Protocols for the use by FTAM
Part 2:   Definition of document types, constraint
sets and syntaxes
DAM 1:   Additional definitions
Part 3:   AFT 11 - Simple File Transfer Service
(unstructured)
Part 4:   AFT12 - Positional File Transfer Service (flat)
Part 5:   AFT22 - Positional File Access Service (flat)
Part 6:   AFT3 - File Management Service

DISP 10608   Information technology - International Standardized
Profile TAnnn - Connection-mode Transport Service
over connectionless-mode Network Service
Part 1:   General overview and
subnetwork-independent requirements
Part 2:   TA51 profile including
subnetwork-dependent requirements for
CSMA/CD Local Area Networks (LANs)

Part 5: TA1111/TA1121 profiles including subnetwork-dependent requirements for X.25 switched data networks us

DISP 10609 Information technology - International Standardized Profiles TB, TC, TD and TE - Connection-mode Transport Service over connection-mode Network Service

Part 1: Subnetwork-type independent requirements for Group TB

Part 2: Subnetwork-type independent requirements for Group TC

Part 3: Subnetwork-type independent requirements for Group TD

Part 4: Subnetwork-type independent requirements for Group TE

Part 5: Definition of profiles TB1111/TB1121

Part 6: Definition of profiles TC1111/TC1121

Part 7: Definition of profiles TD1111/TD1121

Part 8: Definition of profiles TE1111/TE1121

Part 9: Subnetwork-type dependent requirements for Network Layer, Data Link Layer and Physical Layer

DIS 10646 Information processing - Universal coded character set

CD 10728 Information technology - Information Resource Dictionary System (IRDS) Services Interface

CD 10729 Information technology - Open Systems Interconnection - Conformance test suite for the Presentation Layer

Part 1: Test suite structure and test purposes for the Presentation protocol

Part 2: Test suite structure and test purposes for ASN.1 encodings

Part 3: Embedded abstract test suite for the connection-oriented presentation protocol

PDTR 10730 Information technology - Open Systems Interconnection - Tutorial on naming and addressing

CD 10731 Information technology - Open Systems Interconnection - Conventions for the definition of OSI services

CD 10733 Information technology - Telecommunications and information exchange between systems - Specification of the elements of management information related to OSI Network Layer standards

PDTR 10734 Information technology - Open Systems Interconnection - Guidelines for bridged LAN source routing operation by end systems

PDTR 10735 Information technology - Open Systems Interconnection - Standard group MAC addresses

CD 10736 Information technology - Open Systems Interconnection - Specification of the elements of management information related to OSI Transport Layer standards

CD 10737 Information processing systems - Open Systems Interconnection - Transport Layer management

ISO 10739 Information technology - Open Systems Interconnection - Conformance test suite for ISO 9041 - Virtual terminal basic class protocol
Part 1:   Test suite structure and test purposes

DIS 10857 Information technology - Futurebus+ - Logical layer specifications

DIS 10859 Information technology - 8-bit backplane interface: STEbus

DIS 10860 Information technology - Simple 32-bit backplane bus: NuBus

DIS 10861 Information technology - High-performance synchronous 32-bit bus - Multibus II

pDISP 11181 Information technology - International Standardized Profiles AOMnn - OSI management

Part 1:   AOM10 - Specification of ACSE,
            Presentation and Session protocols for use
            by ROSE and CMISE
Part 2:   AOM12 - Enhanced management
            communicationsDT
Part 3:   AOM11 - Basic management
            communicationsD

TR 12382 Information processing - Permuted index of the
              vocabulary of information processing

DIS 25014 Local area network CSMA/CD 10 Mbit/s baseband
               planning and installation guide
               Part 2.1:   Architecture

1.5   IEC STANDARDS

IEC-380   Safety of electrically energized office machines

IEC-381   Analogue signals for process control systems
Part 1:   Direct current signals
Part 2:   Direct voltage signals

IEC-435   Safety of data processing equipment

IEC-516   CAMAC - Modular instrumentation and digital interface system

IEC-547   Specification of modular plug-in unit and standard 19-inch rack mounting unit based on NIM standard

IEC-550   Interface between numerical controls and industrial machines

IEC-552   CAMAC - Organisation of multi-crate systems: specification of the Branch highway and CAMAC crate controller Type A1

IEC-559   Binary floating point arithmetic for microprocessor systems

IEC-625-1   Interface system for programmable measuring apparatus, byte-serial, bit-parallel - functional, electrical and mechanical requirements, system applications and requirements for the designer and user

IEC-625-2   Interface system for programmable measuring apparatus, byte-serial, bit-parallel - code and format conventions

IEC-640   CAMAC - serial highway interface system

IEC-677   Block transfers in CAMAC systems

IEC-678   Definitions of CAMAC terms used in IEC publications

IEC-729   Multiple controllers in a CAMAC crate

IEC-775   CAMAC - Real-time BASIC for CAMAC

IEC-796   Microprocessor system bus - 8-bit and 16-bit data (MULTIBUS I)

      Part 1:   Functional description with electrical and timing specifications

      Part 2:   Mechanical and pin descriptions for the system bus configuration with edge connectors (direct)

      Part 3:   Mechanical and pin description for the Eurocard configuration with pin and socket (indirect) connectors

IEC-821   VME bus - Microprocessor system bus for 1 to 4-byte data

IEC-822   Parallel subsystem bus of the IEC 821 VME bus

IEC-823   Microprocessor system bus (VMSbus) - serial subsystem bus of the IEC 821 bus (VMEbus)

IEC-824   Terminology related to microprocessors

IEC-828   Pin allocations for microprocessor systems using the IEC 603-2 connector

IEC-847   Characteristics of local area networks

IEC-907   Specification for local area networks CSMA/CD 10 Mbit/s baseband planning and installation guide

IEC-950   Safety of information technology equipment including electrical business equipment

IEC-955   Process industry data highway (PROWAY) types A, B and C

2   STANDARDS FROM TRANS-NATIONAL BODIES

2.1   IEEE STANDARDS

IEEE 91   Graphics symbols for logic systems

IEEE 100   Dictionary of electrical and electronics terms

IEEE 162   Definition of terms for electronic digital computers

IEEE 165   Definitions of terms for analog computers

IEEE 166   Definitions of terms for hybrid computer linkage components

IEEE 171   Definitions of terms for information theory

IEEE 280   Letter symbols for quantities used in electronics and electrical engineering

IEEE 281   Standard service conditions for power system communication equipment

IEEE 312   Definitions of terms for communication switching

IEEE 416   ATLAS Test Language

IEEE 446   Recommended practice for emergency and standby power systems for industrial and commercial applications

IEEE 488.1   Digital interface for programmable instrumentation

IEEE 488.2	Standard codes, formats, protocols and common commands for use with ANSI/IEEE Standard 488.1-1987
IEEE 500	Guide to the collection and presentation of electrical, electronic sensing component and mechanical equipment reliability data for nuclear power generating stations
IEEE 583	Modular instrumentation and digital interface system
IEEE 595	Serial highway interface system
IEEE 596	Parallel highway interface system (CAMAC)
IEEE 602	Electrical systems in health care facilities
IEEE 610.2	Glossary of computer applications terminology
IEEE 610.3	Glossary of modeling and simulation terminology
IEEE 660	Semiconductor memory test pattern language
IEEE 662	Standard terminology for semiconductor memory
IEEE 683	Block transfer in CAMAC systems
IEEE 694	Microprocessor assembly language
IEEE 695	Trial-use microprocessor universal format for object modules
IEEE 696	Interface for microcomputer system components interconnected by a 100-line parallel backplane (S-100)
IEEE 716	Guide to the use of C/ATLAS test language
IEEE 717	Guide to the use of C/ATLAS test language syntax
IEEE 726	Real-Time BASIC for CAMAC
IEEE 728	Code and format conventions for use with ANSI/IEEE Standard 488-1978
IEEE 729	Glossary of software engineering terminology

IEEE 730   Software quality assurance plans

IEEE 754   Binary floating-point arithmetic

IEEE 755   Trial-Use Standard for extending high-level language implementations for microprocessors

IEEE 758   Subroutines for CAMAC

IEEE 770   Computer programming language Standard: Pascal

IEEE 771   Guide to the use of ATLAS

IEEE 796   Microcomputer System Bus (Multibus)

IEEE 802.1   Local Network for Computer Interconnection

IEEE 802.2   Local Area Networks: Logical Link Control

IEEE 802.3   Local Area Networks: Carrier Sense Multiple Access with Collision Detection (CSMA/CD)

IEEE 802.3D Local Area Networks: Fiber Optic Inter-Repeater Link

IEEE 802.4   Local Area Networks: Token-Passing Bus Access Method and Physical Layer Specifications

IEEE 802.5   Local Area Networks: Token Ring Access Method and Physical Layer Specifications

IEEE 802.6   Metropolitan Area Networks

IEEE 802.7   [Broadband]

IEEE 802.8   [Fibre Optics]

IEEE 802.9   [Integrated Voice and Data LAN]

IEEE 802.10 [Standard for Interoperable LAN Security]

IEEE 812   Definitions of terms relating to fiber optics

IEEE 828   Software configuration management plans

IEEE 829   Software test documentation

IEEE 830   Guide to software requirements specifications

IEEE 854	Radix-independent floating-point arithmetic
IEEE 855	Microprocessor operating system interfaces (MOSI)
IEEE 896.1	FutureBus - a backplane bus for multiprocessor architectures
IEEE 949	Standard for media-independent information transfer
IEEE 960	FASTBUS modular high-speed data acquisition and control system
IEEE 961	Eight bit microcomputer bus system
IEEE 983	Guide for software Quality Assurance planning
IEEE 990	Ada as a Program Design Language
IEEE 991	Logic circuit diagrams
IEEE 997	Serial ASCII Instrument Loop (SAIL) shipboard data communication
IEEE 1000	8-bit backplane interface: STEbus
IEEE 1002	Taxonomy for software engineering standards
IEEE 1003	Portable operating system for computer environments (POSIX)
IEEE 1003.0	A guide to POSIX Open Systems environments
IEEE 1003.1	System services and C language binding
IEEE 1003.10	Supercomputing Application Environment profile
IEEE 1003.11	Transaction Processing Application Environment profile
IEEE 1003.2	Shell and utility application interface (POSIX)
IEEE 1003.3	Test methods for measuring conformance to POSIX
IEEE 1003.4	Real time POSIX extensions
IEEE 1003.5	Ada bindings
IEEE 1003.6	Security

IEEE 1003.7 System administration interface for computer operating system environment

IEEE 1003.9 FORTRAN bindings

IEEE 1008 Software unit testing

IEEE 1012 Software verification and validation plans

IEEE 1014 Versatile backplane bus (VMEbus)

IEEE 1016 A recommended practice for software design descriptions

IEEE 1042 Guide for software configuration management

IEEE 1058.1 Software project management plans

IEEE 1063 Software user documentation

IEEE 1076 VHDL language reference manual

IEEE 1084 Glossary of mathematics of computing terminology

IEEE 1086 Theory of computing terminology

IEEE 1087 Computing hardware terminology

IEEE 1088 Computing environment terminology

IEEE 1089 Computing methodologies terminology

IEEE 1101 Mechanical core specifications for microcomputers

IEEE 1149.2 Standard testability bus: extended serial digital interface

IEEE 1149.3 Standard testability bus: real-time parallel digital interface

IEEE 1149.4 Standard testability bus: real-time analog interface

IEEE 1192 Standard for microcomputer database language

IEEE 1194.0 Backplane electrical performance standard

IEEE 1194.1 Backplane transceiver logic (BTL) electrical characteristics

IEEE 1196 Simple 32-bit backplane bus: NuBus

IEEE 1209 Recommended practice for the evaluation and use of CASE tools

IEEE 1296 High-performance synchronous 32-bit bus: MULTIBUS II

IEEE 1596 Scalable coherent interface (SCI) standard

2.2   ECMA STANDARDS

ECMA-3   CMC7 printed image specification (2nd edition)

ECMA-4   Flow charts (2nd edition)

ECMA-5   Data interchange on 7-track magnetic tape (3rd edition)

ECMA-6   7-bit coded character set (5th edition)

ECMA-14   Rules for the derivation of 4-bit sets derived from the ECMA 7-bit coded character set

ECMA-16   Basic mode control procedures for data communication systems using the ECMA 7-bit code

ECMA-17   Graphic representation of the control characters of the ECMA 7-bit coded character set for information interchange

ECMA-24   Digital data transmission - code independent information transfer

ECMA-26   Digital data transmission - recovery procedures

ECMA-27   Digital data transmission - abort and interrupt procedures

ECMA-28   Digital data transmission - multiple station select procedures

ECMA-29   Digital data transmission - conversational information message transfer

ECMA-35   Code extension techniques (4th edition)

ECMA-37   Digital data transmission - supplementary transmission control functions

ECMA-40   HDLC frame structure

ECMA-41   Magnetic tape cassette labelling and file structure for information interchange

ECMA-42   Alphanumeric character set for 7 x 9 matrix printers

ECMA-43   8-bit code - structure and rules (2nd edition)

ECMA-48   Control functions for coded character sets (4th edition)

ECMA-49   HDLC elements of procedure

ECMA-50   Programming language PL/1

ECMA-57   Safety Requirements for Data Processing Equipment (2nd edition)

ECMA-60   HDLC unbalanced class of procedure

ECMA-61   HDLC balanced class of procedure

ECMA-71   HDLC selected procedures

ECMA-72   Transport protocol (3rd edition)

ECMA-74   Measurement of airborne noise emitted by computer and business equipment (2nd edition)

ECMA-75   Session protocol

ECMA-80   Local Area Networks (CSMA/CD baseband) - Coaxial cable system (2nd edition)

ECMA-81   Local Area Networks (CSMA/CD baseband) - Physical layer (2nd edition)

ECMA-82   Local Area Networks (CSMA/CD baseband) - Link layer (2nd edition)

ECMA-83   Safety requirements for DTE-to-DCE interface in public data networks (2nd edition)

ECMA-84   Data presentation protocol

ECMA-85   Virtual file protocol

ECMA-86   Generic data presentation - services description and protocol definition

ECMA-87   Generic Virtual Terminal - Service and protocol definition

ECMA-88   Basic class Virtual Terminal - Service description and protocol definition

ECMA-89   Local area networks - token ring technique (2nd edition)

ECMA-90   Local area networks - token bus technique

ECMA-91   Flexible disk cartridges - File structure and labelling for information interchange

ECMA-92   Connectionless Internet protocol

ECMA-93   Distributed Application for Message Interchange (MIDA)

ECMA-94   8-bit single byte coded graphic character set - Latin alphabets No 1 to No 4 (2nd edition)

ECMA-95   Limits of interference and measurement methods

ECMA-96   Syntax of graphical data for multiple workstation interface (GDS)

ECMA-97   Local area networks - safety requirements

ECMA-101   Open document architecture (ODA) and interchange format (2nd edition)

ECMA-102   Rate adaptation for the support of synchronous and asynchronous equipment using the V-series type interface on a PCSN (2nd edition)

ECMA-103   Physical Layer at the Basic Access Interface between data processing equipment and private switching networks (2nd edition)

ECMA-104   Physical Layer at the Primary Rate Access Interface between data processing equipment and private switching networks

ECMA-105   Data Link Layer protocol for the D-channel of the S-interfaces between data processing equipment and private switching networks (2nd edition)

ECMA-106 Layer 3 protocol for signalling over the D-channel of the S-interfaces between data processing equipment and private switching networks

ECMA-108 Measurement of high frequency noise emitted by computer and business equipment

ECMA-109 Declared noise emission values of computer and business equipment (2nd edition)

ECMA-110 Ergonomics - requirement for monochromatic visual display devices

ECMA-112 X.25 (1980) subnetwork-dependent convergence protocol

ECMA-113 8-bit single-byte coded graphic character sets - Latin/Cyrillic alphabet (2nd edition)

ECMA-114 8-bit single-byte coded graphic character sets - Latin/Arabic alphabet

ECMA-115 Common secondary keyboard layout for languages using a Latin alphabet

ECMA-117 Domain Specific Part of Network Layer addresses

ECMA-118 8-bit single-byte coded graphic character sets - Latin/Greek alphabets

ECMA-121 8-bit single-byte coded graphic character set - Latin/Hebrew alphabet

ECMA-122 MIDA - Mailbox service description and mailbox access protocol specification

ECMA-123 In-band parameter exchange in private pre-ISDN networks using Standard ECMA-102

ECMA-126 Ergonomics - requirements for colour visual display devices

ECMA-127 RPC - Basic Remote Procedure Call (RPC) using OSI Remote Operations

ECMA-128   8-bit single-byte coded character sets - Latin alphabet No 5

ECMA-129   Safety of information technology equipment (SITE)

ECMA-131   Referenced data transfer

ECMA-133   Reference configurations for calls through exchanges of private telecommunications networks

2.3 ECMA TECHNICAL REPORTS

TR-13 Network layer principles

TR-14 Local area networks - layers 1 to 4, architecture and protocols

TR-15 Analysis of European X.25 networks

TR-16 Interface characteristics for a DTE to operate with European Recommendation X.25 networks

TR-17 Permission to connect - PTT requirements for obtaining approval to connect apparatus to the network

TR-18 The meaning of conformance to standards

TR-20 Local area networks - layer 4 to 1 addressing

TR-21 Local area networks - interworking units for distributed systems

TR-22 Ergonomics - Recommendations for VDU work places

TR-23 Electrostatic discharge susceptibility

TR-24 Interface between data processing equipment and Private Automatic Branch Exchange

TR-25 OSI sub-network interconnection scenarios permitted within the framework of the ISO-OSI Reference Model

TR-26 Planning and installation guide for CSMA/CD 10 Mbit/s baseband local area network

TR-27 Method for the prediction of installation noise levels

TR-28 Safety verification (SAVE) report ECMA-57/IEC 435

TR-29 Open Systems Interconnection Distributed Interactive Processing Environment (DIPE)

TR-30 Remote Database Access service and protocol

TR-31 Remote Operations - Concepts, notation and connection-oriented mappings

TR-32   OSI directory access service and protocol

TR-34   Maintenance at the interface between data processing equipment and private switching network

TR-35   Particular safety requirements for equipment to be connected to telecommunication networks

TR-37   Framework for OSI Management

TR-38   End system routing

TR-39   Compliance verification (COVER) report (2nd edition)

TR-40   Electrostatic discharge immunity testing of information technology equipment

TR-41   ODA - Document specification language

TR-42   Framework for distributed office applications

TR-43   Packetized data transfer in private switching networks

TR-44   An architectural framework for private networks

TR-45   Information interchange for remote maintenance at the interface between data processing equipment and private switching networks

TR-46   Security in open systems - a security framework

TR-47   Configuration management service definition

TR-48   Study of the translation of the ODA formatted form into Page Description Language

3 EUROPEAN STANDARDS

3.1 CEN STANDARDS

Many CEN Standards are functional profiles (which may then be submitted as International Standardized Profiles). In the following list, a reference in brackets such as "(A/514)" is the classification of the profile, as defined in CEN Memorandum M-IT-02. Documents without a number are proposed profiles in course of preparation.

Information systems interconnection: File Transfer, Access and Management (FTAM); Full file transfer (hierarchical) (A/113)

Information systems interconnection: File Transfer, Access and Management (FTAM); Full file access (hierarchical) (A/123)

Virtual Terminal - Basic Class (A-mode) - Line scrolled (A/4111)

Virtual Terminal - Basic Class (A-mode) - Paged (A/4112)

Virtual Terminal - Basic Class (A-mode) - CCITT X.3 PAD compatible (A/4113)

Virtual Terminal - Basic Class (A-mode) - Transparent (A/4114)

Virtual Terminal - Basic Class (A-mode) - Enhanced line scrolled (A/4115)

Virtual Terminal - Basic Class (A-mode) - Enhanced paged (A/4116)

Virtual Terminal - Basic Class (S-mode) - Forms (A/4121)

Virtual Terminal - Basic Class (S-mode) - Paged (A/4122)

Virtual Terminal - Basic Class (S-mode) - Enhanced forms (A/4123)

Virtual Terminal - Basic Class (S-mode) - Enhanced paged (A/4124)

OSI Management (A/5)

[DUAs and referrals] (A/514)

Remote Database Access (A/6)

Directory - access to centralized directory (A/711)

Directory - Directory System Protocol (A/712)

Directory - Behaviour of DSAs for Distributed Operations (A/713)

Directory - Dynamic behaviour of DUAs (A/714)

Transaction Processing (A/8)

VT Control Objects - Application - Sequenced (Q/411)

VT Control Objects - Application - Unsequenced (Q/412)

VT Control Objects - Terminal - Sequenced (Q/421)

VT Control Objects - Terminal - Unsequenced (Q/422)

VT Control Objects - General (Q/43)

VT Control Objects - General - Terminal condition control object (Q/431)

Directory Application Profile - Common Directory Usage (Q/511)

Directory Application Profile - Directory usage by MHS (Q/512)

Directory Application Profile - Directory usage by FTAM (Q/513)

ISDN (public/private) circuit switched bearer service (CONS case) using B-channel: permanent case (T/1111)

EN 27 372   Trade data interchange: Trade data elements directory

EN 27 498   Open Systems Interconnection Basic Reference Model

EN 27 942   Graphical Kernel System (GKS) functional description

EN 28 877   Interface connector and contact assignments for ISDN basic access interface located at reference points S and T

EN 28 879   Standard Generalized Markup Language (SGML)

EN 29 001   Model for quality assurance in design/ development, production, installation and servicing

EN 29 002   Model for quality assurance in production and installation

EN 29 003   Model for quality assurance in final inspection and test

ENV 29 069   SGML Document Interchange Format (SDIF)

prEN 29 316   Small Computer Systems Interface (SCSI)

EN 29 735   Electronic data interchange for administration, commerce and transport (EDIFACT) - Application level syntax rules

HD 40 001   Requirements for Information Technology
                     Equipment

prENV 40 002   X/Open Portability Guide

ENV 40 003   Computer Integrated Manufacturing (CIM) - CIM
                     system architecture framework for modelling

ENV 41 001   ISDN connector up to 8 pins and up to 2048
                     Mbit/s

ENV 41 003   Particular safety requirements for equipment to be
                     connected to a telecommunication network

prENV 41 004   Reference configuration for calls through
                     exchanges of private telecommunication networks

prENV 41 005   Method for the specification of basic and
                     supplementary services of Private
                     Telecommunication Networks

ENV 41 006   Scenarios for interconnections between
                     exchanges of private telecommunication networks
                     - (1) Inter-PTNX networking scenarios (2)
                     Individual descriptions of the scenarios, impact on
                     the PTN (3) Individual descriptions of the
                     scenarios, impact on the public ISDN

prENV 41 007   Definition of terms in private telecommunication
                     networksDT
                     Part 1:   Definition of general terms

ENV 41 101   Provision of the OSI connection-mode Transport
                     Service using connectionless-mode network
                     service on a CSMA/CD single LAN (T/6211)

EN 41 102   Provision of the OSI connection-mode Transport
                     Service using connectionless-mode network
                     service in an end system attached to a CSMA/CD
                     LAN (T/6212)

ENV 41 103   Provision of the OSI connection-mode Transport
                     Service and the OSI connection-mode network

service in an end system on a CSMA/CD LAN (T/611)

prENV 41 104   Packet Switched Data Networks - Permanent access (T/31)

prENV 41 105   Packet Switched Data Networks - Switched access (T.70 and CONS)

prENV 41 106   Digital data circuit (circuit switched data networks) - Provision of the OSI connection-mode Transport Service in the T.70 case for telematic end systems

prENV 41 107   Digital data circuit (Circuit Switched Data Networks) - Provision of the OSI connection-mode Transport Service and the OSI connection-mode Network Service (T/42)

prEN 41 108   Provision of the OSI connection-mode Transport Service and the OSI connection-mode Network Service in an end system attached to a Token Ring LAN (T/613)

ENV 41 109   Provision of the OSI connection-mode Transport Service using connectionless-mode Network Service on a Token Ring single LAN (T/613)

ENV 41 110   Provision of the OSI connection-mode Transport Service and the OSI Connectionless-mode Network Service in an end system attached to a Token Ring LAN in a single or multiple configuration (T/6232)

prENV 41 111   Provision of OSI connection-mode Transport Service and the OSI connection-mode Network Service by using an ISDN circuit-mode 64 kbit/s unrestricted bearer service - permanent case

prENV 41 112   Provision of the OSI connection-mode Transport Service and the OSI connection-mode Network Service by using an ISDN circuit-mode 64 kbit/s unrestricted bearer service - demand case

ENV 41 201   Private Message Handling Systems - User Agent and Message Transfer Agent - Private Management Domain to Private Management Domain (A/3211)

ENV 41 202   Private Message Handling Systems - User Agent and Message Transfer Agent - Accessing an Administration Management Domain (A/311)

prENV 41 203   Exchange of Teletex documents between two end systems, which may be Teletex terminals (A/221)

prEN 41 204   European Functional Standard A/FT11 - File transfer, access and management - File transfer service: simple (unstructured)

prENV 41 205   Information systems interconnection: File Transfer, Access and Management (FTAM); File Management (A/13)

ENV 41 206   Information systems interconnection: File Transfer, Access and Management (FTAM); Positional file transfer (flat) (A/112)

ENV 41 207   Information systems interconnection: File Transfer, Access and Management (FTAM); Positional file access (flat) (A/122)

ENV 41 208   Basic class virtual terminal - S-mode forms
                      Part 1:   Virtual terminal service (A/4121)
                      Part 2:   Check list (A/4121)
                      Part 3:   Underlying layers check list (A/4121)

ENV 41 209   Basic class virtual terminal - Common control objects (Q/411+)

ENV 41 210   Directory access (A/DI1)

ENV 41 404   Character repertoires for information processing systems interchanging data via Telex

ENV 41 501   Graphic character repertoire and coding for interworking with CEPT videotex services (Q/217)

ENV 41 502	Graphic character repertoire and coding for interworking with CEPT teletex services (Q/214)
prENV 41 503	European graphic character repertoires and their coding (S/13)
prENV 41 504	Character repertoire and coding for interworking with Telex services
prENV 41 505	Graphic character repertoire and coding for line drawing
ENV 41 506	Data stream format for interchange via Telex
ENV 41 507	Data stream format for interchange via Videotex
prENV 41 508	East European character repertoires and their coding
ENV 41 509	Office Document Architecture (ODA) - Document Application Profile - Processable and formattable documents - Basic character content (Q/111)
ENV 41 510	Office Document Architecture (ODA) - Document Application Profile - Processable and formattable documents - Extended mixed mode (Q/112)
ENV 41 511	Office Document Architecture (ODA) - Document Application Profile - Processable and layout-independent documents - Simple messaging profile (Q/121)
ENV 41 512	Common directory use (F/DI1)
DprENV 41 801	Relay - CLNS - LAN/LAN
prENV 41 901	X.29-mode procedures between a packet mode DTE or a PAD and a PAD via a public or private X.25 packet switched network or ISO 8208 packet level entity and ISO 7776 link entity. X.3 character mode access via a public or private PAD attached to an X.25 packet switched network or ISO 8208 packet level entity and ISO 7776 link level entity.

	X.28 character mode access via a telephone circuit or data circuit to a PAD
EN 55 014	Specification for limits and methods of measurements of radio interference characteristics of household electrical appliances, portable tools and similar electrical apparatus
EN 55 022	Limits and methods of measurement of radio interference characteristics of information technology equipment
EN 60 948	Numeric keyboard electronic systems (HES)
EN 60 950	Safety of information technology equipment including electrical business equipment

3.2   ETSI STANDARDS

prETS 300 002   Public Switched Telephone Network (PSTN): approval requirements for 9600 or 4800 bits per second duplex modems standardized for use on the PSTN

prl-ETS 300 003   Transmission characteristics of digital Private Automatic Branch Exchanges (PABXs)

prl-ETS 300 004   Transmission characteristics at 2-wire analogue interface of a digital Private Automatic Branch Exchange (PABX)

prl-ETS 300 005   Transmission characteristics at 4-wire analogue interface of a digital Private Automatic Branch Exchange (PABX)

prl-ETS 300 006   Transmission characteristics at digital interfaces of a digital Private Automatic Branch Exchange (PABX)

prETS 300 007   Integrated Services Digital Network (ISDN): Support of packet mode terminal equipment by an ISDN

prETS 300 008   CCITT signalling system number 7: Message Transfer Part (MTP) to support international interconnection

prETS 300 009   CCITT signalling system number 7: Signalling Connection Control Part (SCCP) [connectionless service] to support international interconnection

prETS 300 010   Synchronous cross connect equipment: 64 and n x 64 kbit/s cross connection rate 2048 kbit/s access ports
Part 1:   Core functions and characteristics

prETS 300 011   Integrated Services Digital Network (ISDN): Primary rate user-network interface: Layer 1 specification and test principles

prETS 300 012   Integrated Services Digital Network (ISDN): Basic user-network interface: Layer 1 specification and test principles

prETS 300 015   Normative Annex to NET 32: Terminal equipment requirements for teletex terminal equipment participating in the teletex service

prETS 300 016   Normative Annex to NET 32: Terminal equipment service intercommunication requirements for teletex terminal equipment participating in a regulated teletex service

prETS 300 017   National tests referenced by NET 32: Terminal equipment test procedures for teletex

prETS 300 019   Equipment engineering - Environmental conditions and environmental tests for telecommunications equipment
Part A: Introduction and terminology
Part B: Classification of enviromental conditions

prI-ETS 300 020   European digital cellular telecommunications system (phase 1)
Part 1:   Mobile station type approval procedure principles
Part 2:   Mobile station conformity specifications
Part 3:   Mobile station conformance test system - system simulator specification

prI-ETS 300 021   European digital cellular telecommunications system (phase 1): mobile station - base station system (MS-BSS) interface data link layer specification

prI-ETS 300 022   European digital cellular telecommunications system (phase 1): mobile radio interface layer 3 specification

prI-ETS 300 023   European digital cellular telecommunications system (phase 1): point to point short message service support on mobile radio interface

prl-ETS 300 024 European digital cellular telecommunications system (phase 1): Short Message Service Cell Broadcast (SMSCB) support on the mobile radio interface

prl-ETS 300 025 European digital cellular telecommunications system (phase 1): Rate adaptation on the Mobile Station - Base Station System (MS-BSS) interface

prl-ETS 300 026 European digital cellular telecommunications system (phase 1): Radio Link Protocol (RLP) for data and telematic services on the Mobile Station - Base Station System (MS-BSS) interface and the Base Station System - Mobile Switching Centre (BSS-MSC) interface

prl-ETS 300 027 European digital cellular telecommunications system (phase 1): Mobile radio interface layer 3 supplementary services specification - formats and coding

prl-ETS 300 028 European digital cellular telecommunications system (phase 1): Mobile radio interface layer 3 call offering supplementary services specification

prl-ETS 300 029 European digital cellular telecommunications system (phase 1): Mobile radio interface layer 3 call restriction supplementary services specification

prl-ETS 300 030 European digital cellular telecommunications system (phase 1): Multiplexing and multiple access on the radio path

prl-ETS 300 031 European digital cellular telecommunications system (phase 1): Channel coding

prl-ETS 300 032 European digital cellular telecommunications system (phase 1): Modulation

prl-ETS 300 033 European digital cellular telecommunications system (phase 1): Radio transmission and reception

prl-ETS 300 034 European digital cellular telecommunications system (phase 1): Radio sub-system link control

prl-ETS 3C0 035 European digital cellular telecommunications system (phase 1): Radio sub-system synchronisation

prl-ETS 300 036 European digital cellular telecommunications system (phase 1): Full-rate speech transcoding

prl-ETS 300 037 European first generation digital cellular tele-communications system - substitution and muting of lost frames for full-rate speech traffic channels

prl-ETS 300 038 European digital cellular telecommunications system (phase 1) - Comfort noise aspects for full-rate speech traffic channels

prl-ETS 300 039 European digital cellular telecommunications system (phase 1) - Discontinuous transmission (DTX) for full-rate speech traffic channels

prl-ETS 300 040 European digital cellular telecommunications system (phase 1) - Voice activity detection

prl-ETS 300 041 European digital cellular telecommunications system (phase 1) - General on terminal adaptation functions for mobile stations

prl-ETS 300 042 European digital cellular telecommunications system (phase 1) - Terminal adaptation functions for services using asynchronous bearer capabilities

prl-ETS 300 043 European digital cellular telecommunications system (phase 1) - Terminal adaptation functions for services using synchronous bearer capabilities

prl-ETS 300 044 European digital cellular telecommunications system (phase 1) - Mobile application part specification

prl-ETS 300 045 European digital cellular telecommunications system (phase 1) - Subscriber Identity Module -

Mobile Equipment (SIM-ME) interface specification

prETS 300 046 Integrated Services Digital Network (ISDN): Primary rate access - safety
Part 1: General
Part 2: Interface 1a: Safety
Part 3: Interface 1a: Protection
Part 4: Interface 1b: Safety
Part 5: Interface 1b: Protection

prETS 300 047 Integrated Services Digital Network (ISDN): Basic rate access - safety and protection
Part 1: General
Part 2: Interface 1a - safety
Part 3: Interface 1a - protection
Part 4: Interface 1b - safety
Part 5: Interface 1b - protection

prETS 300 048 Integrated Services Digital Network (ISDN): ISDN Packet Mode Bearer Service (PMBS). ISDN Virtual Call (VC) and Permanent Virtual Call (PVC) bearer services provided by the B channel of the user access - basic and primary rate

prETS 300 049 Integrated Services Digital Network (ISDN): ISDN Packet Mode Bearer Service (PMBS). ISDN Virtual Call (VC) and Permanent Virtual Call (PVC) bearer services provided by the D channel of the user access - basic and primary rate

prETS 300 050 Integrated Services Digital Network (ISDN): Multiple Subscriber Number (MSN) supplementary service; Service description

prETS 300 051 Integrated Services Digital Network (ISDN): Multiple Subscriber Number (MSN) supplementary service; Functional capabilities and information flows

prETS 300 052 Integrated Services Digital Network (ISDN): Multiple Subscriber Number (MSN) supplementary service; Digital Subscriber Signalling One (DSS1) protocol

prETS 300 053 Integrated Services Digital Network (ISDN): Terminal portability (TP) supplementary service. Service description.

prETS 300 054 Integrated Services Digital Network (ISDN): Terminal portability (TP) supplementary service. Functional capabilities and information flows.

prETS 300 055 Integrated Services Digital Network (ISDN): Terminal portability (TP) supplementary service. Digital Subscriber Signalling One (DSS1) protocol.

prETS 300 056 Integrated Services Digital Network (ISDN): Call Waiting (CW) supplementary service. Service description.

prETS 300 057 Integrated Services Digital Network (ISDN): Call Waiting (CW) supplementary service. Functional capabilities and information flows.

prETS 300 058 Integrated Services Digital Network (ISDN): Call Waiting (CW) supplementary service. Digital Subscriber Signalling One (DSS1) protocol.

prETS 300 059 Integrated Services Digital Network (ISDN): Subaddressing (SUB) supplementary service. Service description.

prETS 300 060 Integrated Services Digital Network (ISDN): Subaddressing (SUB) supplementary service. Functional capabilities and information flows.

prETS 300 061 Integrated Services Digital Network (ISDN): Subaddressing (SUB) supplementary service. Digital Subscriber Signalling One (DSS1) protocol.

prETS 300 062 Integrated Services Digital Network (ISDN): Digital Dialling In (DDI) supplementary service. Service description.

prETS 300 063 Integrated Services Digital Network (ISDN): Digital Dialling In (DDI) supplementary service. Functional capabilities and information flows.

prETS 300 064 Integrated Services Digital Network (ISDN): Digital Dialling In (DDI) supplementary service. Digital Subscriber Signalling One (DSS1) protocol.

prETS 300 065 Narrow-band direct-printing telegraph equipment for receiving mereorological or navigational information (NAVTEX). Technical characteristics and methods of measurement.

prETS 300 066 Float-free maritime satellite emergency position-indicating radio beacons (EPIRMs) operating on 406.025 MHz. Technical characteristics and methods of measurement.

ETS 300 067 Radiotelex equipment operating in the maritime MF/HF service. Technical characteristics and methods of measurement.

prI-ETS 300 068 European digital cellular telecommunications system (phase 1) - Man-machine interface of the mobile station.

prI-ETS 300 069 European digital cellular telecommunications system (phase 1) - Technical realization of the short message service. Cell broadcast.

ETS 300 072 Terminal equipment (TE): videotex presentation layer protocol: videotex presentation layer data syntax

ETS 300 073 Videotex presentation layer data syntax: Geometric display

ETS 300 074 Videotex presentation layer data syntax: Transparent data

ETS 300 075 Terminal equipment (TE): Videotex processable data

ETS 300 076   Terminal equipment (TE): Videotex: Terminal Facility Identifier (TFI)

prETS 300 077   Integrated Services Digital Network (ISDN): Attachment requirements for terminal adaptors to connect to an ISDN at the S/T reference point

prl-ETS 300 078 European digital cellular telecommunications system (phase 1) - Layer 1 - general requirements

prETS 300 079   Integrated Services Digital Network (ISDN): Syntax-based videotex. End-to-end protocols

prETS 300 080   Integrated Services Digital Network (ISDN): ISDN lower layer protocols for telematic terminals

prETS 300 081   Integrated Services Digital Network (ISDN): Teletex end-to-end protocol over the ISDN

prETS 300 082   Integrated Services Digital Network (ISDN): 3.1 kHz telephony teleservice. End-to-end compatibility.

prETS 300 083   Integrated Services Digital Network (ISDN): Circuit mode structured bearer service category usable for speech information transfer. End-to-end comptability.

prETS 300 084   Integrated Services Digital Network (ISDN): Circuit mode structured bearer service category usable for 3.1 kHz audio information transfer. End-to-end comptability.

prETS 300 085   Integrated Services Digital Network (ISDN): 3.1 kHz telephony teleservice. Attachment requirements for handset terminals.

prETS 300 086   Radio Equipment and Systems. Land mobile service. Technical characteristics and test conditions for radio quipment with an internal or external RF connector intended primarily for analogue speech.

prETS 300 087 Integrated Services Digital Network (ISDN): Facsimile group 4 class 1 equipment on the ISDN. Functional specification of the equipment (T/TE 05-09)

prETS 300 088 Integrated Services Digital Network (ISDN): Facsimile group 4 class 1 equipment on the ISDN. General and service aspects (T/TE 05-06)

prETS 300 089 Integrated Services Digital Network (ISDN): Calling Line Identification Presentation (CLIP) supplementary service. Service description.

prETS 300 090 Integrated Services Digital Network (ISDN): Calling Line Identification Restriction (CLIR) supplementary service. Service description.

prETS 300 091 Integrated Services Digital Network (ISDN): Calling Line Identification, Presentation and Restriction (CLIP and CLIR) supplementary service. Functional capabilities and information flows.

prETS 300 092 Integrated Services Digital Network (ISDN): Calling Line Identification Presentation (CLIP) supplementary service. Digital Subscriber Signalling one (DSS1) protocol.

prETS 300 093 Integrated Services Digital Network (ISDN): Calling Line Identification Restriction (CLIR) supplementary service. Digital Subscriber Signalling one (DSS1) protocol.

prETS 300 094 Integrated Services Digital Network (ISDN): Connected Line Identification Presentation (COLP) supplementary service. Service description.

prETS 300 095 Integrated Services Digital Network (ISDN): Connected Line Identification Restriction (COLR) supplementary service. Service description.

prETS 300 096 Integrated Services Digital Network (ISDN): Connected Line Identification, Presentation and

Restriction (COLP and COLR) supplementary service. Functional capabilities and information flows.

prETS 300 097 Integrated Services Digital Network (ISDN): Connected Line Identification Presentation (COLP) supplementary service. Digital Subscriber Signalling one (DSS1) protocol.

prETS 300 098 Integrated Services Digital Network (ISDN): Connected Line Identification Restriction (COLR) supplementary service. Digital Subscriber Signalling one (DSS1) protocol.

prETS 300 099 Integrated Services Digital Network (ISDN): Specification of the Packet Handler Access Point Interface (PHI) for the provision of prETS 300 007 (CCITT Recommendation X.31) packet mode services.

prETS 300 100 Integrated Services Digital Network (ISDN): Routing. In support of the ISDN Memorandum of Understanding (T/N 23-03).

prETS 300 101 Integrated Services Digital Network (ISDN): International Digitail Audiographic Teleconference

prETS 300 102 Integrated Services Digital Network (ISDN): User-network interface layer 3.
Part 1:   Specifications for basic call control.
Part 2:   Specifications for basic call control.
            Specification Description Language
            (SDL) diagrams.

prETS 300 103 Integrated Services Digital Network (ISDN): Support of CCITT Recommendations X.21, X.21*bis* and X.20*bis* based Data Terminal Equipments (DTEs) by an ISDN. Synchronous and asynchronous terminal adaption functions.

prETS 300 104 Integrated Services Digital Network (ISDN): Attachment requiremer.ts for terminal equipment to connect to an ISDN using ISDN basic access. Layer 3 aspects.

prETS 300 105   Terminal equipment (TE): Videotex interworking

prETS 300 106   Terminal equipment (TE): International interworking between a terminal and a host

prETS 300 107   Terminal equipment (TE): International interworking between gateways

prETS 300 108   Integrated Services Digital Network (ISDN): Circuit-mode 64 kbit/s unrestricted 8 kHz structured bearer service category. Service description.

prETS 300 109   Integrated Services Digital Network (ISDN): Circuit-mode 64 kbit/s 8 kHz structured bearer service category. Service description.

prETS 300 110   Integrated Services Digital Network (ISDN): Circuit-mode 64 kbit/s 8 kHz structured bearer service category (T/NA1(89)37) usable for 3.1 kHz audio information transfer. Service description.

prETS 300 111   Integrated Services Digital Network (ISDN): Telephony 3.1 kHz teleservice. Service description.

prETS 300 112   Integrated Services Digital Network (ISDN): Facsimile group 4 class 1 equipment on the ISDN. End-to-end protocols.

prETS 300 113   Radio Equipment and Systems. Land mobile service. Technical characteristics and test conditions for non-speech and combined analog speech/non-speech equipment with an internal or external antenna connector, intended for the transmission of data

prETS 300 114   Attachments to the Public Switched Telephone Network (PSTN). Basic attachment requirements for modems standardized for use on the PSTN.

prETS 300 115   Attachments to the Public Switched Telephone Network (PSTN). Category II attachment requirements for 300 bits per second duplex modems standardized for use on the PSTN.

prETS 300 116   Attachments to the Public Switched Telephone Network (PSTN). Category II attachment requirements for 1200 bits per second duplex modems standardized for use on the PSTN.

prETS 300 117   Attachments to the Public Switched Telephone Network (PSTN). Category II attachment requirements for 2400 bits per second duplex modems standardized for use on the PSTN.

prETS 300 118   Attachments to the Public Switched Telephone Network (PSTN). Category II attachment requirements for 1200 bits per second half duplex modems and 1200/75 bits per second asymmetrical duplex modems standardized for use on the PSTN.

prETS 300 120   Integrated Services Digital Network (ISDN): Telefax G4

prETS 300 121   Integrated Services Digital Network (ISDN): Application of the ISDN user part of CCITT Signalling System No 7 for the international ISDN interconnections (CCITT Recommendation Q.767 draft, modified)

prETS 300 122   Integrated Services Digital Network (ISDN): Generic keypad protocol for the support of supplementary services. Digital Subscriber Signalling one (DSS1) protocol

prETS 300 123   Attachment requirements for Data Terminal Equipment (DTE) to connect to Packet Switched Public Data Networks (PSPDN) using CCITT Recommendation X.25(1984) interface. Requirements applicable to DTEs subscribing to modulo 128 operation.

prETS 300 124 Attachment requirements for Data Terminal Equipment (DTE) to connect to Packet Switched Public Data Networks (PSPDN) using CCITT Recommendation X.25(1984) interface. Requirements applicable to DTEs subscribing to multilink operation.

prETS 300 125 Integrated Services Digital Network (ISDN): User-network interface data link layer specifications. Application of CCITT Recommendations Q.920/I.440 and Q.921/I.441

prETS 300 126 Integrated Services Digital Network (ISDN): equipment with ISDN interface at basic and primary rate. EMC requirements.

prETS 300 127 Equipment engineering. Radiated emission testing of physically large systems.

prETS 300 128 Integrated Services Digital Network (ISDN): malicious call identification (MCID) supplementary service. Service description.

prETS 300 129 Integrated Services Digital Network (ISDN): malicious call identification (MCID) supplementary service. Functional capabilities and information flows.

prETS 300 130 Integrated Services Digital Network (ISDN): malicious call identification (MCID) supplementary service. Digital Subscriber Signalling One (DSS1) protocol.

prETS 300 131 Radio equipment and systems. Second generation cordless telephones. Common air interface specification to be used for the interworking between cordless telephone apparatue including public access services.

prETS 300 134 Integrated Services Digital Network (ISDN): CCITT Signalling System No 7. Transaction Capabilities Application Part (TCAP).

prETS 300 136   Integrated Services Digital Network (ISDN): Closed User Group (CUG) supplementary service. Service description.

prETS 300 137   Integrated Services Digital Network (ISDN): Closed User Group (CUG) supplementary service. Functional capabilities and information flows.

prETS 300 138   Integrated Services Digital Network (ISDN): Closed User Group (CUG) supplementary service. Digital Subscriber Signalling one (DSS1) protocol.

prETS 300 139   Integrated Services Digital Network (ISDN): Call Hold (HOLD) supplementary service. Service description.

prETS 300 140   Integrated Services Digital Network (ISDN): Call Hold (HOLD) supplementary service. Functional capabilities and information flows.

prETS 300 141   Integrated Services Digital Network (ISDN): Call Hold (HOLD) supplementary service. Digital Subscriber Signalling one (DSS1) protocol.

prETS 300 142   Integrated Services Digital Network (ISDN) and other digital telecommunications networks. Audiovisual teleservices. Video codec for audio visual services at p*64 Kbit/s (T/N 31-04)

prETS 300 143   Integrated Services Digital Network (ISDN) and other digital telecommunications networks. Audiovisual teleservices. System for establishing communication between audiovisual terminals using digital channels up to 2048 kbit/s (T/N 32-03)

prETS 300 144   Integrated Services Digital Network (ISDN) and other digital telecommunications networks. Audiovisual teleservices. Frame structure for a 64 to 1920 kbit/s channel (T/N 32-04)

prETS 300 145   Integrated Services Digital Network (ISDN) and other digital telecommunications networks. Audiovisual teleservices. Narrowband visual telephone systems (T/N 32-05)

prETS 300 146   Integrated Services Digital Network (ISDN) and other digital telecommunications networks. Audiovisual teleservices. Frame synchronous control and indication signals for audiovisual systems (T/N 32-06)

prETS 300 147   Transmission and multiplexing. Synchronous digital hierarchy. Multiplexing structure (DE/TM-3001)

prETS 300 148   Terminal Equipment (TE): Requirements for Teletex systems participating in the Teletex service (T/TE 07-10)

prETS 300 149   Terminal Equipment (TE): Videotex. Audio syntax (T/TE 06-07)

prETS 300 150   Transmission and multiplexing. Protocol suites for Q interfaces for management of transmission systems (DE/TM-2001)

prETS 300 153   Integrated Services Digital Network (ISDN): Attachment requirements for terminal equipment to connect to an ISDN using ISDN basic access (T/TE 04-08)

prETS 300 154   Terminal Equipment (TE): Optional applications between teletex equipments. Transparent mode and local dispatching at the receiving side (T/TE 07-09)

prETS 300 155   Integrated Services Digital Network (ISDN): Facsimile group 4 class 1 equipment on the ISDN. End-to-end protocol tests (T/TE 05-08)

prETS 300 156   Integrated Services Digital Network (ISDN): Attachment requirements for terminal equipment to connect to an ISDN using ISDN primary rate access (T/TE 04-24)

4   NATIONAL STANDARDS BODIES

4.1   BSI STANDARDS

BS 3862   Recommendations for symbols for languages, geographical areas and authorities

BS 3939   Guide for graphical symbols for electrical power, telecommunications and electronic diagrams
Part 1:   General information and general index
Part 2:   Symbol elements, qualifying symbols and other symbols having general application
Part 3:   Conductors and connecting devices
Part 4:   Passive components
Part 5:   Semiconductors and electron tubes
Part 6:   Production and conversion of electrical energy
Part 7:   Switchgear, controlgear and protective devices
Part 8:   Measuring instruments, lamps and signalling devices
Part 9:   Telecommunications: switching and peripheral equipment
Part 10:   Telecommunications: transmission
Part 11:   Architectural and topographicalinstallation plans and diagrams
Part 12:   Binary logic elements
Part 13:   Analogue elements

BS 4280   Transliteration of Arabic characters

BS 4335   Glossary of terms used in project network techniques

BS 4505   Digital data transmission
　　　　　　　Part 1:　　Specification for basic mode control
　　　　　　　　　　　　procedures
　　　　　　　Part 2:　　Character structure for start/stop and
　　　　　　　　　　　　synchronous transmission
　　　　　　　Part 3:　　Method for use of longitudinal parity to
　　　　　　　　　　　　detect errors in information messages
　　　　　　　Part 4:　　Basic mode control procedures - code
　　　　　　　　　　　　independent information transfer
　　　　　　　Part 6:　　Complements to the basic mode control
　　　　　　　　　　　　procedures; recovery, abort and interrupt,
　　　　　　　　　　　　multiple station selection
　　　　　　　Part 7:　　Basic mode control procedures;
　　　　　　　　　　　　conversational information message transfer

BS 4730   Specification for the United Kingdom 7-bit coded
character set

BS 4731   Specification for derivatives of the United Kingdom 7-bit
data code

BS 4760   Specification for numbering of weeks

BS 4812   Specification for the Romanization of Japanese

BS 4822   Specification for keyboard arrangements of the graphic
characters of the United Kingdom 7-bit data code for
data processing

BS 5231   Specification for principles governing the positioning of
control keys on keyboards of office machines and data
processing equipment

BS 5249   Representation of elements of data in interchanges
using data processing systems
　　　　　　　Part 1:　　Representation of dates and times
　　　　　　　Part 2:　　Representation of human sexes
　　　　　　　Part 3:　　Representation of latitude, longitude and
　　　　　　　　　　　　altitude for geographic point locations

BS 5374   Specification for codes for the representation of names
of countries

BS 5397   High-level data link control (HDLC) procedures
Part 1:   Specification frame structure
Part 2:   Specification for elements of procedures
Part 5:   Specification for consolidation of classes of
          procedures
Part 6:   Specification for multilink procedures
Part 7:   Specification for X.25 LAPB compatible DTE
          data link procedures
Part 8:   Specification for frame level address
          assignment
Part 9:   Specification for general purpose XID
          information field content and format
          (including parameters for parameter
          negotiation and multilink subfields)

BS 5448   Specification for keyboard layouts for numeric
applications on office machines and data processing
equipment

BS 5549   Specification of modular plug-in unit and standard 19
inch rack mounting unit based on NIM standard (for
electronic nuclear instruments)

BS 5554   Guide to a modular instrumentation system for data
handling; CAMAC system

BS 5555   Specification for SI units and recommendations for the
use of their multiples and of certain other units

BS 5750   Quality systems
Part 0:   Principal concepts and applications
Part 1:   Specification for design/development,
          production, installation and servicing
Part 2:   Specification for production and installation
Part 3:   Specification for final inspection and test
Part 4:   Guide to the use of BS 5750

BS 5760   Reliability of constructed or manufactured products,
systems, equipments and components
Part 0:   Introductory guide to reliability
Part 1:   Guide to reliability and maintainability
          programme management
Part 2:   Guide to the assessment of reliability

	Part 3:	Guide to reliability practices: examples
	Part 4:	Guide to specification clauses relating to the achievement and development of reliability in new and existing items

BS 5775 Specification for quantities, units and symbols
- Part 0: General principles
- Part 1: Space and time
- Part 2: Periodic and related phenomena
- Part 3: Mechanics
- Part 4: Heat
- Part 5: Electricity and magnetism
- Part 6: Light and related electromagnetic radiations
- Part 7: Acoustics
- Part 8: Physical chemistry and molecular physics
- Part 9: Atomic and nuclear physics
- Part 10: Nuclear reactions and ionizing radiations
- Part 11: Mathematical signs and symbols for use in the physical sciences and technology
- Part 12: Dimensionless parameters

BS 5836 Guide to CAMAC - Organisation of multi-crate systems: specification of the Branch highway and CAMAC crate controller Type A1

BS 5850 Specification for safety of electrically energised office machines

BS 5863 Analogue signals for process control systems
- Part 1: Specification for direct current signals
- Part 2: Specification for direct voltage signals

BS 5870 Recommendations for line spacings and character spacings for office machines and data processing equipment

BS 5887 Code of practice for testing of computer-based systems

BS 6006 Specification for structure and rules for implementation of United Kingdom 8-bit coded character set

BS 6046   Use of network techniques in project management
                 Part 1:   Guide to the use of management, planning,
                            review and reporting procedures

BS 6238   Code of practice for the performance monitoring of
                 computer-based systems

BS 6301   Specification for electrical safety requirements for
                 apparatus for connection to certain telecommunication
                 networks

BS 6305   Specification for general requirements for apparatus for
                 connection to the British Telecommunications public
                 switched telephone network

BS 6317   Specification for simple telephones for connection to
                 public switched telephone networks run by certain
                 telecommunications operators

BS 6320   Specification for modems for connection to the British
                 Telecommunications public switched telephone
                 network

BS 6328   Apparatus for connection to private circuits run by
                 certain public telecommunications operators
                 Part 1:   Specification for apparatus for connection
                            to speechband circuits
                 Part 2:   Specification for apparatus for connection
                            to baseband circuits
                 Part 3:   Specification for apparatus for connection
                            to wideband (FDM) circuits
                 Part 8:   Specification for apparatus for connection
                            to digital circuits with interfaces according
                            to CCITT G-series Recommendations
                            Section 8.1: G.703

BS 6390   Specification for a set of functions for computer
                 graphics programming - the Graphical Kernel System
                 (GKS)

BS 6403   Specification for simple telex terminals using SCVF signalling for connection to the British Telecommunications telex network

BS 6429   Method of conversion between the ISO 7-bit coded character set (ISO 646) and the CCITT international telegraph alphabet No 2 (ITA 2)

BS 6430   Method for representing SI and other units in information processing systems with limited character sets

BS 6450   Private branch exchanges for connection to public switched telephone networks run by certain public telecommunications operators
              Part 1:   Specification for general requirements
              Part 2:   Specification for PBXs with terminating stations treated as an entirety
              Part 5:   Facilities on PBXs
              Part 6:   Simple call-routing mode (SCRM)
              Part 7:   Specification for the procedure for in-service observation of PBXs undergoing type approval

BS 6474   Coded character sets for bibliographic information interchange
              Part 1:   Specification for extension of the Latin alphabet coded character set
              Part 2:   Specification for Greek alphabet coded character set
              Part 3:   Specification for African coded character set
              Part 4:   Specification for extension of the Cyrillic alphabet coded character set

BS 6475   Specification for processor system bus interface (Eurobus A)

BS 6484   Specification for electrical safety requirements for independent power supply units for indirect connection to certain telecommunication networks

BS 6488   Code of Practice for configuration management of computer-based systems

BS 6493   Semiconductor devices
Part 2:   Integrated circuits

BS 6514   Guide for implementation of V.24 or RS-232 as an asynchronous local interface

BS 6527   Specification for limits and methods of measurement of radio interference characteristics of information technology equipment

BS 6531   10 Mbps slotted ring local area network
Part 1:   Specification for the coding of bits and structure of slots and mini-packets
Part 2:   Specification for configuration
Part 3:   Specification for free-standing repeaters
Part 4:   Specification for basic and enhanced class nodes with type 1 node/DTE interface
Part 5:   Specification for monitor
Part 6:   Specification for logging station
Part 7:   Specification for slave power supplies

BS 6532   Data terminal equipment for attachment to 10 Mbps slotted ring local area network
Part 1:   Specification for media access control procedures for data terminal equipment
Part 2:   Specification for implementation requirements for media access control in general purpose data terminal equipment

BS 6541   Specification for check character systems for use in information interchange and guidance on choice and methods of application

BS 6568   Information Processing Systems - Open Systems Interconnection - Basic Reference Model
Part 1:   Basic Reference Model (incorporating connectionless-mode transmission)

BS 6623   DTE/DCE interface connectors and pin assignments
Part 4:   34-pin connector

BS 6636   Message types for securities
Part 1:   Specification for messages for
receipt/delivery
Part 2:   Specification for messages for orders to
buy/sell

BS 6638   Guide to transmission signal quality at the DTE/DCE
interface
Part 1:   Start-stop signal quality
Part 2:   Synchronous transmission

BS 6639   Guide to DTE/DCE interface control operation using
the 25 pole connector

BS 6640   Guide to arrangements for DTE to DTE physical
connection
Part 1:   General arrangements for DTE-DTE
physical connection using V.24 and X.24
interchange circuits
Part 2:   DTE-DTE physical connection using X.24
interchange circuits with DTE provided
timing

BS 6650   Code of Practice for the control of the operation of a
computer

BS 6667   Electromagnetic compatibility for industrial-process
measurement and control equipment
Part 1:   General introduction
Part 2:   Method of evaluating susceptibility to
electrostatic discharge
Part 3:   Method of evaluating susceptibility to
radiated electromagnetic energy

BS 6690   Specification for a data descriptive file for information
interchange

BS 6692   Coded character sets for text communication
Part 1:   General introduction
Part 2:   Specification for Latin alphabetic and
non-alphabetic graphic characters
Part 3:   Specification for control functions for
page-image format

BS 6701   Code of practice for installation of apparatus intended for connection to certain telecommunications systems
Part 1:   General recommendations
Part 2:   Installation of switching apparatus that may be connected to certain analogue telecommunications systems

BS 6727   Information processing systems - Specification for representation of numerical values in character strings for information interchange

BS 6789   Apparatus with one or more particular functions for connection to public switched telephone networks run by certain public telecommunications operators
Part 1:   General requirements
Part 2:   Specification for apparatus with loudspeaking facilities
Part 3:   Apparatus with auto-calling, auto-answering and auto-clearing facilities
Part 6:   Specification for series connected apparatus
Part 7:   Specification for apparatus with call barring facilities

BS 6822   Specification for format for transmission of certificate numbers of securities

BS 6856   Specification for code extension techniques for United Kingdom 7-bit and 8-bit coded character sets

BS 6868   Specification for Standard Generalized Markup Language (SGML) for text and office systems

BS 6940   Total access communication system (TACS)
Part 1:   Performance requirements for mobile stations
Part 2:   Performance and tests of the signalling system of mobile stations

BS 6945   Specification for computer graphics: metafile for the storage and transfer of picture description information (CGM)
Part 1:   Functional specification
Part 2:   Character encoding

Part 3:   Binary encoding
Part 4:   Clear text encoding

BS 6960   Open Systems Interconnection: Basic connection-oriented session service definition

BS 6961   Open Systems Interconnection: Basic connection-oriented session protocol specification

BS 6962   Open Systems Interconnection: Specification for Abstract Syntax Notation One (ASN.1)

BS 6963   Open Systems Interconnection: Specification for basic encoding rules for Abstract Syntax Notation One (ASN.1)

BS 6964   Specification for database language SQL

BS 7002   Specification for safety of data processing equipment

BS 7040   Computer graphics: Graphical Kernel System (GKS) language bindings
Part 1:   Specification for GKS language binding for FORTRAN
Part 2:   Specification for GKS language binding for Pascal

BS 7090   Open Systems Interconnection: file transfer, access and management
Part 1:   General introduction
Part 2:   Virtual filestore definition
Part 3:   File service definition
Part 4:   File protocol definition

BS 7091   Open Systems Interconnection: service definition for the Association Control Service Element

BS 7092   Open Systems Interconnection: protocol specification for the Association Control Service Element

BS 7093   Open Systems Interconnection: connection-oriented presentation service definition

BS 7094   Open Systems Interconnection: connection-oriented presentation protocol specification

BS 7095   Specification for codes for the representation of currencies and funds

BS 7096   Guide to design and use of bank cards with a magnetic stripe that employs track 3

BS 7097   Procedure for allocating an international securities identification number (ISIN)

BS 7107   Procedure for allocating international issuer identification numbers (IINs) for use on identification cards

BS 7108   Guide to design and use of identification cards as financial transaction cards

BS 7109   Guide to design and use of identification cards having integrated circuits with contacts
Part 3:   Electronic signals and transmission
                 protocols

BS 7112   British Standard procedures for achievement of interoperability and security by use of encipherment at the Physical Layer of OSI in telecommunication systems conveying automatic data processing information

BS 7151   Specification for representation of dates and times in information interchange

BS 7179   Ergonomics of design and use of visual display terminals (VDTs) in offices
Part 1:   Introduction
Part 2:   Recommendations for the design of office
                 VDT tasks
Part 3:   Specification for visual displays
Part 4:   Specification for keyboard
Part 5:   Specification for VDT workstations
Part 6:   Code of practice for the design of VDT
                 work environments

BS 7205   Procedures for key management to achieve security for financial institutions engaged in financial transactions (wholesale)

BS 7218	Open Systems Interconnection: Transport Service definition (incorporating connectionless-mode transmission)
BS 7220	Information processing systems: Data communications: Network Service definition
BS 7221	Internal organization of the Network Layer
BS 7222	Open Systems Interconnection: connectionless-mode transport protocol specification
BS 7224	Specification for use of X.25 to provde the OSI connection-mode network service
BS 7226	Information processing systems - Interface connector and contact assignments for ISDN basic access interface located at reference points S and T
BS 7232	Specification for information exchange systems: End system to intermediate system routeing exchange protocol for use in conjunction with the protocol for providing the connecitonless-mode network service
BS 7233	Fibre Distributed Data Interface (FDDI) Part 1: Specification for token ring physical layer protocol (PHY)
BS 7235	Open Systems Interconnection: Specification for protocol to provide the connectinless-mode network service
BS 7237	Specification for binary floating point arithmetic for microprocessor systems
BS 7237	Glossary for terminology related to microprocessors
BS 7240	Specification for pin allocations for microprocessor systems using the IEC 603-2 connector
BS 7241	IEC 822 VSB. Parallel sub-system bus of the IEC 821 VME bus
BS 7242	IEC 821 Bus. Microprocessor system bus for 1 to 4 byte data.

BS 7245   Numeric keyboard for home electronic systems (HES)

BS 7246   Guide for local area networks CSMA/CD 10 Mbit/s baseband planning and installation

BS 7247   Guide for characteristics of local area networks (LANs)

BS 7248   Multipoint interconnection of data communications equipment by twisted pair cable

BS 7266   Connectors for access to the Integrated Services Digital Network (ISDN)
Part 1:   Specification for a Basic Access Interface connector and its contact assignments

BS 7267   Open Systems Interconnection: Guide to operation of an X.25 interworking unit

BS 7292   Specification for layout and operation of keyboards for multiple Latin-alphabet languages

BS 7298   Schedule of requirements and recommendations for cards to be used in electronic funds transfer at point of sale (EFT-POS)

BS 7299   Office Document Architecture (ODA) and interchange format for text and office systems
Part 1:   Introduction and general principles
Part 2:   Document structures
Part 4:   Document profile
Part 5:   Office document interchange format (ODIF)
Part 6:   Character content architectures
Part 7:   Raster graphics content architectures
Part 8:   Geometric graphics content architectures

BS 7301   Specification for programming language: APL

BS 7302   Specification for micro-processor universal format object modules

BS 7306   The operation of the UK scheme for the allocation of ISO DCC format OSI NSAP addresses (including the operation of the UK Registration Authority)

BS 7362 Specification for telex terminal apparatus for connection to public telecommunications operators' telex networks

4.2 ANSI STANDARDS

X3.1-1987   Information Systems - Data Transmission - Synchronous signaling rates

X3.4-1986   Coded character sets - 7-bit American National Standard Code for information interchange

X3.15-1976   Bit sequencing of the American National Standard Code for Information Interchange in serial-by-bit data transmission

X3.16-1976   Character structure and character parity sense for serial-by-bit data communication in the American National Standard Code for Information Interchange

X3.24   Signal Quality at interface between data terminal equipment and synchronous data circuit-terminating equipment for serial data transmission

X3.25-1976   Character structure and character parity sense for parallel-by-bit data communication in the American National Standard Code for Information Interchange

X3.28-1976   Procedures for the use of the communication control characters of American National Standard Code for Information Interchange in specified data communications links

X3.30-1985   Representation of calendar date and ordinal date for information interchange

X3.32-1973   Graphic representation of the control characters of the American National Standard Code for Information Interchange

X3.36-1975   Synchronous high-speed data signaling rates between data terminal equipment and data communication equipment

X3.41-1974 Code extension techniques for use with the 7-bit coded character set of American National Standard Code for Information Interchange

X3.42-1975 Representation of numeric values in character strings for information interchange

X3.43-1986 Representation of local time of the day for information interchange

X3.44-1974 Determination of the performance of data communication systems

X3.51-1986 Representations of Universal Time, local time differentials and United States time zone references for information interchange

X3.57-1977 Structure for formatting message headings for information interchange using the American National Standard Code for Information Interchange for data communication system control

X3.61-1986 Representation of geographic point locations for information interchange

X3.64-1979 Additional controls for use with the American National Standard Code for Information Interchange

X3.66-1979 Advanced Data Communication Control Procedures (ADCCP)

X3.79-1981 Determination of performance of data communication systems that use bit-oriented control procedures

X3.91-1987 Storage module interfaces

X3.92-1981 Data encryption algorithm

X3.98-1983 Text information interchange in Page Image Format (PIF)

X3.100-1983 Interface between Data Terminal Equipment and Data Circuit-Terminating Equipment for packet mode operation with packet switched data communication networks

X3.102-1983   Data communication systems and services - user oriented performance parameters

X3.105-1983   Data link encryption

X3.106-1983   Modes of operation for the Data Encryption Algorithm

X3.107-1982   Data Link Layer protocol for local distributed data interfaces

X3.108-1982   Physical Layer interface for local distributed data interface to a non-branching coaxial cable bus

X3.109-1982   Physical Layer protocol for local distributed data interfaces

X3.110-1983   Videotex/Teletext Presentation Level Protocol syntax (North American PLPS)

X3.117-1984   Information systems - Text and facsimile communication equipment - printable/image areas

X3.122-1986   Computer Graphics - Metafile for the storage and transfer of Picture Description Information

X3.124-1985   Graphical Kernel System (GKS) - Functional Description
Part 1:   Pascal language binding

X3.125-1985   Computer graphics - Graphical Kernel System (GKS) FORTRAN binding

X3.128   Contact Start/Stop Storage Disk

X3.129-1986   Intelligent Peripheral Interface - Physical Level

X3.130-1986   Intelligent Peripheral Interface - Device-specific command set for magnetic disk drives

X3.131-1986   Small Computer System Interface (SCSI)

X3.132-1987	Intelligent Peripheral Interface - Device-generic command set for magnetic and optical disks
X3.133-1986	Network Database Language
X3.134.1-1986	8-bit ASCII structure and rules
X3.134.2-1986	7-bit and 8-bit ASCII supplemental multilingual graphic character set (ASCII multilingual set)
X3.135-1989	Information Systems - Database language SQL with integrity enhancement
X3.138-1986	Information Resource Dictionary System (IRDS)
X3.139-1987	Fiber-distributed data interface (FDDI) token ring media access control (MAC)
X3.140-1986	Open Systems Interconnection - Connection-oriented Transport Layer protocol specification
X3.141-1987	Data Communication Systems and Services - measurement methods for user-oriented performance evaluation
X3.143-1985	Standard Generalized Markup Language (SGML)
X3.144-1986	Programmer's Hierarchical Interactive Graphics System (PHIGS) Part 1: FORTRAN language binding Part 3: Ada binding Part 4: C binding
X3.146-1987	Device Level Interface for Streaming Cartridge and Cassette Tape Drives
X3.147-1987	Intelligent Peripheral Interface - Device-generic command set for magnetic tape
X3.148-1986	FDDI Physical Layer Protocol
X3.153-1986	Open Systems Interconnection - Basic connection-oriented session protocol specification

X3.166-198x   A standard for fiber-distributed data interface (FDDI)

X3.168-1989   Information Systems - Database Language - Embedded SQL

X3.170-1988   Enhanced Small Device Interface (ESDI)

X3.177-198x   Intelligent peripheral interface device generic command set for communications

X9.1   Magnetic striped card data content

X9.4   Scannable bill line

X9.5   Financial institution numbering system

X9.9   Financial institution message authentication

X9.17   Financial institution key management (wholesale)

X12.1-1986   Business data interchange - purchase order transaction set

X12.2-1986   Business data interchange - invoice transaction set

X12.3-1986   Business data interchange - data element dictionary

X12.4-1986   Business data interchange - remittance/payment advice transaction set

X12.6-1986   Business data interchange - application control structure

5   CROSS-REFERENCE LISTING OF STANDARDS

ISO	CCITT	BSI	ANSI	IEEE	ECMA	CEN/CLC
233		4280				
639		3862				
646		4730				
963					14	
1001		4732			13	
1004		4810				
1073-1		5464-1			8	
1073-2		5464-2			11	
1090		2481-2				
1091		2481-3				
1092		5478-1				
1093		5478-3				
1154		3880-2				
1155		4505-3				
1177		4505-2				
1539		7146				EN 21 539
1729		3880				
1745		4505-1			16	
1831					15	
1858		3732-2				

ISO	CCITT	BSI	ANSI	IEEE	ECMA	CEN/CLC
1860		3732-1				
1989		7147				EN 21 989
2014		5249-1				
2022		6856			35	
2033		5464-3				
2047					17	
2110		6623-1				
2111		4505-4			24	
2132		5479-1				
2133		5479-2				
2145		5848				
2195		3880-4				
2257		5519-2				
2258		5519-1				
2382		3527				
2382-5		BITS 413				
2382-19		BITS 412				
2530		4822				
2593		6623-4				
2628		4505-6				
2629		4505-7			29	
2775		5519-3				
2784		4623				
2806		6135				
2864		4850-1			32	
2894		5132-1				
2955		6430				
3166		5374				

ISO	CCITT	BSI	ANSI	IEEE	ECMA	CEN/CLC
3244		5231				
3309		5397-1				
3407		5079				
3535		5537				
3540		5519-4				
3554		5132-2				
3561		4850-2			33	
3562		5356-1			38	
3563		5356-2			39	
3564		5359-1				
3791		5448				
3792		5478-2				
3802		3732-3				
3883		5560				
4057		6003			46	
4169		5959				
4217		7095				
4232-1		5960				
4232-2		6050				
4232-3		6191-4				
4335		5397-2				
4337		5395-1			45	
4341		5769-1			41	
4873		6006				
4902		6623-2				
4903		6623-3				
4909		7096				EN 24 909
5138-2		5479-3				

ISO	CCITT	BSI	ANSI	IEEE	ECMA	CEN/CLC
5138-3		6191-3				
5138-4		6191-1				
5138-5		6191-2				
5218		5249-2				
5426		6474-1				
5428		6474-1				
5653		5395-2			52	
5654					54	
5963		6529				
6093		6727				
6160		7148				EN 26 160
6166		6602				
6234		6321				
6260		6601				
6373		7149				EN 26 373
6429		DD 94			48	
6438		6474-3				
6596					66	
6709		5249-3				
6901					64	
6902					65	
6937		6692				
6939		6429				
6951		6475				
7064		6541				
7065					69	
7154		6478				
7185						EN 27 185

ISO	CCITT	BSI	ANSI	IEEE	ECMA	CEN/CLC
7297					73	
7298					76	
7299					77	
7341		6695				
7372						EN 27 372
7477		6640-1				
7478		5397-6				
7480		6638-1				
7487		7024			70	EN 27 487
7498	X.200	6568				EN 27 498
7498 AD1		DD 125				
7498-2		BITS 294				
7498-3		BITS 344				
7498-4		BITS 429				
7665		6542			91	
7775		6636				
7776		5397-7				
7809		5397-5				
7810						EN 27 810
7811						EN 27 811
7812		7107				EN 27 812
7813		7108				EN 27 813
7816						EN 27 816
7846		6831				
7942		6390	X3.124			EN 27 942
8036		7081				
8064					68	
8072	X.214	7218				

ISO	CCITT	BSI	ANSI	IEEE	ECMA	CEN/CLC
8073	X.224	7223				
8109		BITS 710				
8208		7219				
8211		6690				
8326	X.215	6960				
8326 DAD1			BITS 293			
8326 DAD2			BITS 507			
8326 DAD3			BITS 508			
8327	X.225	6961	X3.153			
8327 DAD1			BITS 292			
8327 DAD2			BITS 509			
8348	X.213	7220				
8378		7023			78	EN 28 378
8462					98	
8471-2		5397-8				
8473		7235				
8473 PDAD 2			BITS 418			
8480		6639				
8481		6640-2				
8482		7248				
8484		7110				
8485		7301				
8509	X.210	DD 108				
8532		6822				
8571		7090				
8601		7151				
8602		7222				
8613		7299			101	

ISO	CCITT	BSI	ANSI	IEEE	ECMA	CEN/CLC
8613-1	T.411					
8613-2	T.412					
8613-4	T.414					
8613-5	T.415					
8613-6	T.416					
8613-7	T.417					
8613-8	T.418					
8630					99	
8632		6945				
8648-2		7221				
8649	X.217	7091				
8649 PDAD1			BITS 727			
8649 PDAD2			BITS 547			
8650	X.227	7092				
8650 PDAD1			BITS 728			
8650 PDAD2			BITS 721			
8651		7040	X3.125			
8652		7145				EN 28 652
8732		7205				
8802-2		DD 99-1		802.2		
8802-3		BITS 417		802.3		
8802-3 DAD1			BITS 420			
8802-4		BITS 416		802.4		
8802-5		DD 136-1		802.5		
8805		BITS 280				
8806-1		BITS 111				
8807		BITS 345				
8822	X.216	7093				

ISO	CCITT	BSI	ANSI	IEEE	ECMA	CEN/CLC
8822 PDAD1			BITS 452			
8823	X.226	7094				
8824	X.208(88)	6962				
8824 PDAD1			BITS 505			
8825	X.209(88)	6963				
8825 PDAD1			BITS 505			
8831		BITS 654				
8832		BITS 655				
8860		6958			100	EN 28 860
8867-2		BITS 714				
8877-2		DD 144				
8877		7266-1				EN 28 877
8878	X.223	7224				
8879		6868				EN 28 879
8880		DD 141				
8881		DD 142				
8882-1		BITS 090				
8882-2		BITS 512				
8882-3		BITS 513				
8883		BITS 152				
8885		5397-9				
8886	X.212	DD 145				
8907		BITS 244	X3.133			
9040		BITS 638				
9040 AD1		BITS 700				
9041		BITS 348				
9041 DAD1			BITS 365			
9065	X.420(88)					

ISO	CCITT	BSI	ANSI	IEEE	ECMA	CEN/CLC
9066-1	X.218					
9066-2	X.228					
9067		7249				
9068		BITS 093				
9069		9069				EN 29 069
9072-1	X.219					
9072-2	X.229					
9074		BITS 701				
9075		6964	X3.135			
9075 DAD1			BITS 295			
9293		6542				EN 29 293
9314-1		7233-1				
9316						EN 29 316
9320		BITS 414				
9506-1		BITS 704				
9506-2		BITS 705				
9506-5		BITS 706				
9506-6		BITS 707				
9542		7232				
9543		6638-2				
9545	X.207	BITS 634				
9548		BITS 510				
9571		BITS 656				
9572		BITS 657				
9574	X.223bis(88)					
9576		BITS 454				
9592-1		BITS 297	X3.144.1			
9593-1		BITS 296				

ISO	CCITT	BSI	ANSI	IEEE	ECMA	CEN/CLC
9594-1	X.500	BITS 478				
9594-2	X.501	BITS 479				
9594-3	X.511	BITS 480				
9594-4	X.518	BITS 481				
9594-5	X.519	BITS 482				
9594-6	X.520	BITS 483				
9594-7	X.521	BITS 484				
9594-8	X.509	BITS 485				
9595	X.710	BITS 359				
9596	X.711	BITS 633				
9636-1		BITS 113				
9636-2		BITS 114				
9636-3		BITS 115				
9636-4		BITS 116				
9636-5		BITS 117				
9636-6		BITS 118				
9646	X.290					
9646-1		BITS 630				
9646-2		BITS 631				
9646-4		BITS 496				
9646-5		BITS 497				
9660		7061				EN 29 660
9661		7062				
9796		BITS 408				
9797		BITS 409				
9799		BITS 411				
9804	X.237	BITS 502				
9805	X.247	BITS 690				

ISO	CCITT	BSI	ANSI	IEEE	ECMA	CEN/CLC
9834-1		BITS 708				
9834-2		BITS 495				
9834-4		BITS 450				
9834-5		BITS 451				
9834-6		BITS 719				
9983		BITS 427				
10021-1	X.400	BITS 581				
10021-2	X.402	BITS 582				
10021-3	X.407	BITS 583				
10021-4	X.411	BITS 584				
10021-5	X.413	BITS 585				
10021-6	X.419	BITS 586				
10021-7	X.420	BITS 587				
10022	X.211	BITS 467				
10023		BITS 470				
10024		BITS 471				
10025		BITS 468				
10026-1		BITS 635				
10026-2		BITS 636				
10026-3		BITS 637				
10027		BITS 658				
10029		7267				
10031-1		BITS 692				
10031-2		BITS 693				
10032		BITS 498				
10033		BITS 553				
10035		BITS 546				
10040	X.701	BITS 653				

ISO	CCITT	BSI	ANSI	IEEE	ECMA	CEN/CLC
10148					127	
10164-1	X.730	BITS 650				
10164-2	X.731	BITS 651				
10164-3	X.732	BITS 652				
10164-4	X.733	BITS 649				
10164-5		BITS 646				
10164-7	X.736					
10164-8	X.736					
10164-9	X.740					
10164-11	X.739					
10165-1		BITS 709				
10165-2	X.721	BITS 647				
10165-3		BITS 648				
10166-1		BITS 640				
10166-2		BITS 641				
10168-1		BITS 665				
10168-4		BITS 720				
10175-1		BITS 724				
10175-2		BITS 723				
10450		BITS 722				
10646		BITS 694				

IEC	CCITT	BSI	ANSI	IEEE	ECMA	CEN/CLC
559		7237				
821		7242				
822		7241				
824		7238				
828		7240				
847		7247				
907		7246				
948		7245				
975		7302				

PART III

ACRONYMS AND ABBREVIATIONS

A

A-Profile	Application Profile
A/D	Analogue to Digital
AA	Abort Accept
AARE	ACSE-Associate-Request
AARQ	ACSE-Associate-Request
AAT	Arbitrated Access Timer
ABM	Asynchronous Balanced Mode
ABME	Asynchronous Balanced Mode Extended
ACID	Atomicity, Consistency, Isolation and Durability
ACIT	Adaptive Sub-Band Excited Transform
ACK	Acknowledgment
ACM	Association for Computing Machinery
ACR	Access Control Register
ACSE	Association Control Service Element
ACSNET	Australian Computer Science Network
ACU	Automatic Call Unit
ADC	Analogue-to-Digital Converter
ADCCP	Advanced Data Communication Control Procedure
ADI	Application Data Interchange
ADMD	Administration Management Domain
ADP	Automatic Data Processing
ADPCM	Adaptive Differential Pulse Code Modulation
AE	Application-Entity
AEI	Application-Entity Invocation
AFI	Authority and Format Identifier
AFNOR	Association Francaise de Normalisation
ALS	Application Layer Structure
AM	Amplitude Modulation
AM	Amendment (ISO)
AME	Amplitude Modulation Equivalent
AMI	Alternate Mark Inversion
AMT	Advanced Manufacturing Technologies
ANA	Article Number Association
ANSI	American National Standards Institute
ANTIOPE	l'Acquisition Numérique et Télévisualisation d'Images Organisée en Pages d'Ecriture
AOW	Asia-Oceania Workshop

AP	Anomalous Propagation
AP	Application-Process
APC	Adaptive Predictive Coding
APDU	Application Protocol Data Unit
API	Application-Process Invocation
API	Application Program Interface
AQAP	Allied Quality Assurance Publications (NATO)
ARM	Asynchronous Response Mode
ARP	Address Resolution Protocol
ARPA	Advanced Research Projects Agency (of US Department of Defense)
ARPANET	Advanced Research Projects Agency Network
ARQ	Automatic Request for Repetition
ASA	American Standards Association (now ANSI)
ASCII	American Standard Code for Information Interchange
ASE	Application Service Element
ASK	Amplitude Shift Keying
ASN	Abstract Syntax Notation
ASP	Abstract Service Primitive
ASR	Automatic Send/Receive (terminal)
ATDM	Asynchronous Time Division Multiplexing
ATE	Automatic Testing Equipment
ATM	Abstract Test Method
ATS	Abstract Test Suite
AUI	Attachment Unit Interface
AUTODIN	AUTOmatic DIgital Network (US Department of Defense)
AUTOVON	Automatic Secure Voice Network
AWGN	Additive White Gaussian Noise

B

BABT	British Approvals Board for Telecommunications
BACS	Bankers' Automated Clearing Services
BAS	Basic Activity Subset

BCC	Block Control Character
BCC	Block Check Code
BCD	Binary Coded Decimal
BCI	Bit Count Integrity
BCS	Basic Combined Subset
BEB	Binary Exponential Backoff
BER	Bit Error Rate
BER	Basic Encoding Rules
BERT	Bit Error Rate Test
BISAM	Basic Indexed Sequential Access Method
BISYNC	Binary Synchronous Communication
BITNET	Because It's Time Network
BIU	Basic Information Unit
BLERT	Block Error Rate Test
bps	Bits per second
BS	British Standard
BSI	British Standards Institution
BSP	Byte Stream Protocol
BSS	Basic Synchronized Subset
BT	British Telecom

C

C/I	Channel to Interference ratio
C/N	Carrier to Noise ratio
CAN	Cancel
CAP	Cable Access Point
CASE	Common Application Service Elements
CBC	Cipher Block Chaining
CBX	Computer-Controlled Branch Exchange
CC	Country Code
CCETT	Centre Commun d'Etudes de Télévision et Télécommunications
CCH	Connections per Circuit Hour
CCH	Co-ordination Committee for Harmonisation

CCIR	Comité Consultatif International Radio
CCIS	Common Channel Interoffice Signalling
CCITT	Comité Consultatif International Télégraphique et Téléphonique
CCO	Context Control Object
CCR	Commitment, Concurrency and Recovery
CCTA	Central Computer and Telecommunications Agency (UK)
CCTS	Co-ordination Committee for Satellite Tele-communications
CD	Committee Draft (ISO)
CDMA	Code Division Multiple Access
CDS	Conceptual Data Store
CDT	Connectionless Data Transmission
CEC	Commission of the European Communities
CECC	CENELEC Electronic Components Committee
CEN	Comité Européen de Normalisation
CENCER	Association Certification Comité Européen de Normalisation
CENELEC	Comité Européen de Normalisation Electrotechnique
CEPT	Conférence Européene des Administration des Postes et des Télécommunications
CGI	Computer Graphics Interface
CGM	Computer Graphics Metafile
CILE	Call Information Logging Equipment
CIM	Computer Integrated Manufacturing
CLNP	Connectionless Mode Network Protocol
CLNS	Connectionless Mode Network Service
CLS	Close
CMDR	Command Reject
CMIP	Common Management Information Protocol
CMIPDU	Common Management Information Protocol Data Unit
CMIS	Common Management Information Service
CMISE	Common Management Information Service Element
CMRR	Common Mode Rejection Ratio
CNET	Centre National d'Etudes des Télécommunications
CNMA	Communications Network for Manufacturing Applications
CNR	Common Network Representation
CODEC	Coder-Decoder
COMSAT	Communications Satellite

COMSEC	Communications Security
CONS	Connection-Oriented Network Service
COS	Corporation for Open Systems
COSINE	Co-operation for Open Systems Interconnection Networking in Europe
COST	Cooperation Européene Scientifique et Technique
CPODA	Contention Priority Oriented Demand Assignment
cps	Characters per second
cps	Cycles per second
CR	Carriage Return
CRC	Cyclic Redundancy Check
CSA	Client Service Agent (MHS)
CSC	Circuit Switching Centre
CSDN	Circuit Switched Data Network
CSMA	Carrier-Sense Multiple Access
CSMA-CA	Carrier-Sense Multiple Access - Collision Avoidance
CSMA-CD	Carrier-Sense Multiple Access - Collision Detection
CSMA-CP	Carrier-Sense Multiple Access - Collision Prevention
CSN	Common Subnet Node
CSNET	Computer Science Network
CSNP	Communication Subnet Processors
CSS	Conceptual Signalling and Status Store
CSU	Circuit Switching Unit
CTCA	Channel to Channel Adaptor
CTNE	Compania Telefonica Nacional de España (Spanish PTT)
CTS	Clear to send
CUG	Closed User Group
CVSD	Continuously Variable Slope Delta Modulation

D

D/A	Digital to Analogue
DAC	Digital-to-Analogue Converter
DAC	Data Authentication Code

DAD	Draft Addendum (ISO)
DAF	Framework for Distributed Applications
DAM	Draft Amendment (ISO)
DAMA	Demand Assignment Multiple Access
DAP	Data Access Protocol
DAP	Directory Access Protocol
DARPA	Defense Advanced Research Projects Agency
DASE	Directory Access Service Element
DASS	Digital Access Signalling System
dB	Decibel
DC	Device Control
DCC	Data Country Code
DCD	Data Carrier Detect
DCE	Data Circuit-Terminating Equipment
DCPSK	Differentially Coherent Phase Shift Keying
DCS	Digital Command Signal
DCS	Defense Communications System
DCS	Defined Context Set
DCTN	Defense Commercial Telecommunication Network
DCU	Device Control Unit
DD	Draft for Development (BSI)
DDD	Direct Distance Dialling
DDLCN	Distributed Double-Looped Computer Network
DDN	Digital Data Network
DDN	Defense Data Network
DDP	Distributed Data Processing
DDS	Digital Data Service
DEE	Data Encryption Equipment
DEL	Delete
DES	Data Encryption Standard
DFC	Data Flow Control
DFR	Document Filing and Retrieval
DFSK	Double Frequency Shift Keying
DIA	Document Interchange Architecture
DIAL	Device Independent Access Level
DIANE	Direct Information Access Network - Europe
DID	Data Identifier
DIN	Deutsches Institut für Normung
DIP	Dual In-Line Package
DIS	Draft International Standard
DISP	Draft International Standardized Profile (ISO)

DLC	Data Link Control
DLC	Digital Loop Carrier
DLCN	Distributed Loop Computer Network
DLE	Data Link Escape
DM	Disconnected Mode (HDLC)
DNIC	Destination Network Identification Code
DOAM	Distributed Office Application Model
DOD	Department of Defense (USA)
DOD	Direct Outward Dialling
DOV	Data Over Voice
DP	Draft Proposal
DPA	Document Printing Architecture
DPNSS	Digital Private Network Signalling System
DPSK	Differential Phase Shift Keying
DQDB	Distributed Queue Dual Bus
DRCS	Dynamically Redefinable Character Set
DSA	Directory Service Agent
DSDC	Direct Services Dialling Capability
DSE	Data Switching Exchange
DSI	Digital Speech Interpolation
DSMA	Distributed Scheduling Multiple Access
DSP	Domain Specific Part
DSP	Directory Service Protocol
DSR	Data Set Ready
DSS1	Digital Subscriber Signalling One
DSSE	Directory System Service Element
DSSSL	Document Style Semantics and Specification Language
DSTE	Data Subscriber Terminal Equipment
DTC	Draft Technical Corrigendum
DTE	Data Terminal Equipment
DTMF	Dual Tone Multifrequency (signalling)
DTP	Data Transfer Protocols
DTR	Data Terminal Ready
DTR	Draft Technical Report (ISO)
DUP	Data User Parts (ISDN)

E

EAN	European Article Number
EBCDIC	Extended Binary Coded Decimal Interchange Code
EC	European Community
ECE	Economic Commission for Europe (UN)
ECITC	European Committee for IT Testing and Certification
ECMA	European Computer Manufacturers' Association
ECSA	Exchange Carriers Standards Association
EDI	Electronic Data Interchange
EDIFACT	Electronic Data Interchange for Administration, Commerce and Transport
EEC	European Economic Community
EEUA	Electrical Equipment Users Association
EFT	Electronic Funds Transfer
EFTPOS	Electronic Funds Transfer at Point of Sale
EFTS	Electronic Funds Transfer Service
EHF	Extremely High Frequency
EIA	Electronic Industries Association
EIN	European Informatics Network
EMUG	European MAP Users Group
EN	Européene Norme (European Standard)
ENE	Enterprise Networking Event
ENQ	Enquiry
ENV	Européene Norme Vorausgabe (European Pre-standard)
EOA	End of Address
EOB	End of Block
EOF	End Of File
EOJ	End Of Job
EOM	End Of Message
EOR	End Of Record
EOT	End Of Transmission
EOT	End Of Tape
EOV	End Of Volume
EPAD	Error-Protecting Packet Assembler/Disassembler
EPHOS	European Procurement Handbook on Open Systems
EPOS	Electronic Point-of-Sale
ERP	Effective Radiated Power

ESA	European Space Agency
ESC	Escape
ESDI	Enhanced Small Device Interface
ESPRIT	European Strategic Programme for Research and Development in Information Technology
ET	Exchange Termination (ISDN)
ETB	End of Transmission Block
ETCOM	European Testing and Certification for Office and Manufacturing Protocols
ETS	European Telecommunications Standard
ETSI	European Telecommunications Standards Institute
ETX	End of Text
EUCATEL	European Conference of Associations of Telecommunications Industries
EUREKA	European Research Coordination Agency
EURONET	European On-Line Information Network
EWICS	European Workshop on Industrial Computer Systems
EWOS	European Workshop for Open Systems

F

f-	femto-
F-Profile	Interchange Format and Representation Profile
FADU	File Access Data Unit
FAP	File Access Protocol
FAX	Facsimile
FCC	Federal Communications Commission (USA)
FCS	Frame Check Sequence (HDLC)
FD(X)	Full Duplex
FDDI	Fibre Distributed Data Interface
FDM	Frequency Division Multiplexing
FDMA	Frequency Division Multiple Access
FDT	Formal Description Technique
FDX	Full Duplex

FEC	Forward Error Correction
FF	Form Feed
FIF	Facsimile Information Field
FIFO	First-in, first-out
FIPS	Federal Information Processing Standard
FM	Frequency Modulation
FPDU	FTAM Protocol Data Unit
FPIS	Forward Propagation Ionospheric Scatter
FPLA	Field Programmable Logic Array
FPODA	Fixed Priority Oriented Demand Assignment
FRMR	Frame Reject
FS	File Separator
FSA	Fixed Slot Acknowledgement
FSCS	Functional Standard Conformance Statement
FSK	Frequency Shift Keying
FSM	Finite State Machine
FTAM	File Transfer, Access and Management
FTF	File Transfer Facility
FTP	File Transfer Protocol
FTS	Federal Telecommunications System
FTSC	Federal Telecommunications Standards Committee

G

G-	Giga-
GDAP	Government Document Application Profile
GDN	Government Data Network
GKS	Graphical Kernel System
GLOTOS	Graphical (representation of) Language for Temporal Ordering Specification
GOSIP	Government OSI Profile
GS	Group Separator
GSC	Group Switching Exchange
GSTN	General Switched Telephone Network
GUS	Guide to the Use of Standards (SPAG)

H

HD	Harmonisation Document (CEN/CENELEC)
HD(X)	Half Duplex
HDLC	High-Level Data Link Control
HSLN	High-speed Local Network
Hz	Hertz (cycles/second)

I

IAn	International Alphabet n
IBC	Integrated Broadband Communications
IBCN	Integrated Broadband Communications Network
ICD	International Code Designator
ICP	Initial Connection Protocol
ID	Identifier (or Identification)
IDA	Integrated Digital Access
IDE	Interchange Data Elements
IDI	Initial Domain Identifier
IDN	Integrated Digital Network
IDP	Initial Domain Part
IEC	International Electrotechnical Commission
IEE	Institution of Electrical Engineers (UK)
IEEE	Institute of Electrical and Electronics Engineers (USA)
IFIP	International Federation for Information Processing
I-ETS	Interim European Telecommunication Standard
IFRB	International Frequency Registration Board
IGES	Initial Graphics Exchange Specification
ILAN	Industrial Local Area Network
IMP	Interface Message Processor (ARPANET)
INCA	Integrated Network Communication Architecture
INF	ISDN Numbering Forum
INLP	Inactive Network Layer Protocol

INRIA	Institute Nationale de Récherche d'Informatique et d'Automatique
INTAP	Interoperatbility Technology Association for Information Technology
INTELSAT	International Telecommunications Satellite organisation
IP	Internet Protocol
IPDU	Internetwork Protocol Data Unit
IPI	Intelligent Peripheral Interface
IPM	Interpersonal Messaging
IPSIT	International Public Sector IT Group
IPSS	International Packet SwitchStream
IPTC	International Press Telecommunications Council
IRC	International Record Carrier(s)
IRDS	Information Resource Dictionary System
IRIA	Institute de Récherche d'Informatique et d'Automatique
IRS	Internetwork Routing Service
IRV	International Reference Version
IS	International Standard
ISBX	Integrated Services Branch Exchange
ISD	International Subscriber Dialling
ISDN	Integrated Services Digital Network
ISLN	Integrated Services Local Network
ISO	International Standards Organisation
ISP	International Standardized Profile
ISPBX	Integrated Services Private Branch Exchange
ISPICS	ISP Implementation Conformance Statement
ISR	Information Storage and Retrieval
IT	Information Technology
ITA	International Telegraph Alphabet
ITAEG	Information Technology Ad-hoc Expert Group
ITAEGM	Information Technology Ad-hoc Expert Group for Advanced Manufacturing Technologies
ITAEGS	Information Technology Ad-hoc Expert Group for OSI Functional Standardisation
ITAEGT	Information Technology Ad-hoc Expert Group for Telecommunications
ITSTC	Information Technology Steering Committee
ITSTC	International Telecommunications Standards Technical Council
ITU	International Telecommunications Union

ITUSA   Information Technology Users Standards Association (UK)
IUT   Implementation Under Test

J

JANET   Joint Academic Network
JEDI   Joint Electronic Data Interchange
JITEC   Joint Information Technology Experts Committee
JITM   Joint Information Technology Management Group
JNT   Joint Network Team (UK)
JTC   Joint Technical Committee (ISO/IEC)
JTM   Job Transfer and Manipulation
JTPC   Joint Technical Programs Committee

K

K   Kilo- (one thousand)
KDC   Key Distribution Centre

L

LAN	Local Area Network
LAP	Link Access Protocol
LAP-B	Link Access Protocol - Balanced
LBT	Listen Before Talk
LC	Lower case
LC	Link Control
LCGN	Logical Channel Group Number
LCN	Local Computer Network
LCN	Loosely Coupled Network
LDDI	Local Distributed Data Interface
LF	Low Frequency
LIFO	Last-In, First-Out
LLC	Logical Link Control
LME	Layer Management Entity
LOTOS	Language for Temporal Ordering Specification
LPC	Linear Predictive Coding
LPDU	Link Layer Protocol Data Unit
LRC	Longitudinal Redundancy Check
LSAP	Local Service Access Point
LSB	Least Significant Bit
LSDU	Link Service Data Unit
LLWT	Listen While Talk

M

M	Mega- (one million)
MA-ASE	Multiple Association Application Service Element
MAC	Medium Access Control
MACE	MAP Advisory Centre Europe
MACF	Multiple Association Control Function
MAF	Multiple Access Facility

MAN	Metropolitan Area Network
MAP	Microprocessor Applications Project
MAP	Manufacturing Automation Protocol
MAPDU	Management Application Protocol Data Unit
MAU	Media Access Unit
MCVF	Multi-Channel Voice Frequency
MD	Management Domain
MF	Multi-Frequency
MFM	Modified Frequency Modulation
MFSK	Multiple Frequency Shift Keying
MHS	Message Handling Systems
MHz	Megahertz
MIB	Management Information Base
MIDA	Message Interchange Distributed Application
MIE	Management Information Element
MIL-STD	Military Standard
MIP	Management Information Protocol
MIS	Management Information System
MIT	Management Information Tree
MMFS	Manufacturing Message Format Standard
MMS	Manufacturing Messaging Standard
MO	Managed Object
MOCS	Managed Object Conformance Statement
MODEM	Modulator-Demodulator
MOT	Means of Testing
MOTI	Message Oriented Text Interchange
MOTIS	Message-Oriented Text Interchange Systems
MPCC	Multi-Protocol Communications Controller
MPDU	Message Protocol Data Unit
MPX	Multiplex
ms	Millisecond
MS	Message Store
MSB	Most Significant Bit
MT	Message Transfer
MTA	Message Transfer Agent
MTAE	Message Transfer Agent Entity
MTBF	Mean Time Between Failure
MTF	Message Transfer Facility
MTL	Message Transfer Layer
MTP	Message Transfer Protocol
MTR	Multiple Token Ring

MTS	Message Transfer System
MTSL	Message Transfer Sublayer
MTTF	Mean Time To Failure
MTTR	Mean Time To Repair
MUX	Multiplex(or)

N

NABTS	North American Broadcast Teletext Standard
NACP	North Atlantic Consultative Process
NAK	Negative Acknowledgment
NAM	Network Access Machine
NAPLPS	North American Presentation Level Protocol Syntax
NAU	Network Addressable Unit
NBH	Network Busy Hour
NCC	Network Control Centre
NCP	Network Control Protocol
NDL	Network Database Language
NE	Negotiated Exit
NET	Norme Européene de Télécommunications
NETRJE	Network Remote Job Entry
NETS	Normes Européene de Télécommunication
NFS	Network File Server
NIST	National Institute for Standards and Technology
NIU	Network Interface Unit
NJCL	Network Job Control Language
NMC	Network Measurement Centre
NMM	Network Measurement Machine
NOS	Network Operating System
NPAI	Network Protocol Addressing Information
NPDA	Network Problem Determination Application (SNA)
NPDN	Nordic Public Data Network
NPDU	Network Protocol Data Unit
NPL	National Physical Laboratory (UK)
NPR	Noise to Power Ratio

NRS	Name Registration Scheme
NSA	National Security Agency (USA)
NSAP	Network Service Access Point
NSDU	Network Service Data Unit
NSE	Network Service Element
NSF	National Science Foundation
NSP	Network Services Protocol
NT	Network Termination
NTA	Norwegian Telecommunications Agency
NTIA	National Telecommunications and Information Administration
NTO	Network Terminal Option
NTT	Nippon Telephone and Telegraph Corporation
NTU	Network Termination Unit
NUA	Network User Address
NUI	Network User Identification
NUL	Null
NUN	Network User Name
NVDM	Network Virtual Data Manager
NVDML	Network Virtual Data Management Language
NVT	Network Virtual Terminal

O

O/R	Originator or Recipient
ODA	Open (Office) Document Architecture
ODIF	Open (Office) Document Interchange Format
ODP	Open Distributed Processing
OFTEL	Office of Telecommunications
OIW	OSI Implementors Workshop
OMUP	Organisation and Management User Parts (ISDN)
ONA	Open Network Architecture (BT)
ONR	Office of Naval Research (USA)
OPDU	Operation Protocol Data Unit

ORACLE	Optional Reception of Announcements by Coded Line Electronics
OS	Operating System
OSCL	Operating System Control Language
OSI	Open Systems Interconnection
OSIE	OSI Environment
OSITOP	Open Systems Interconnection Technical and Office Protocols
OSTC	Open Systems Testing Consortium
OSTI	Office for Scientific and Technical Information

P

p-	pico-
PABX	Private Automatic Branch Exchange
PACX	Private Automatic Computer Exchange
PAD	Packet Assembler/Disassembler
PAGODA	Profile Alignment Group on ODA
PAI	Protocol Addressing Information
PAM	Pulse Amplitude Modulation
PAT	Priority Access Timer
PATBX	Private Automatic Telegraph Branch Exchange
PAX	Private Automatic Exchange
PBX	Private Branch Exchange
PCI	Protocol Control Information
PCM	Pulse Code Modulation
PCO	Point of Control and Observation
PCSN	Private circuit-switching network
PCTR	Protocol Conformance Test Report
PDAD	Proposed Draft Addendum (ISO)
PDAM	Proposed Draft Amendment (ISO)
PDISP	Proposed Draft International Standardized Profile (ISO)
PDM	Pulse Duration Modulation
PDN	Public Data Network
PDTR	Proposed Draft Technical Report (ISO)

PDU	Protocol Data Unit
PEP	Peak Envelope Power
PFM	Pulse Frequency Modulation
PHIGS	Programmer's Hierarchical Interactive Graphics System
PIC	Personal Identification Code
PICS	Protocol Implementation Conformance Statement
PIXIT	Protocol Implementation eXtra Information for Testing
PLAN	Personal Local Area Network
PLANET	Private Local Area Network
PLP	Packet Level Protocol
PLTXAU	Public Telex Access Unit
PM	Phase Modulation
PMA	Physical Medium Attachment
PMD	Physical Medium Dependent Layer (FDDI)
PODA	Priority Oriented Demand Assignment
POTS	Plain Old Telephone System
PPCI	Presentation-protocol-control-information
PPDU	Presentation-Protocol-Data-Unit
PPI	Programmable Peripheral Interface
PPM	Pulse Position Modulation
PPM	Presentation Protocol Machine
PPSN	Public Packet Switching Network
PRMD	Private Management Domain
PRN	Packet Radio Network
ps	picosecond
PS	Presentation Service
PSAP	Presentation Service Access Point
PSDN	Packet Switched Data Network
PSDU	Presentation-Service-Data-Unit
PSE	Packet Switching Exchange
PSK	Phase Shift Keying
PSN	Public Switched Network
PSN	Packet Switched Network
PSS	Packet SwitchStream
PSTN	Public Switched Telephone Network
PTM	Pulse Time Modulation
PTN	Private Telecommunication Network
PTNX	Private Telecommunication Network Exchange
PTT	Post, Telegraph and Telephone Administration
PVC	Permanent Virtual Circuit
PWM	Pulse Width Modulation

PhSAP	Physical Service Access Point
PoS	Point of Sale

Q

QA	Quality Assurance
QAM	Quadrature Amplitude Modulation
QC	Quality Control
QPSK	Quadrature Phase Shift Keying
QPSX	Queued Packet Synchronous Exchange
QSAM	Quadrature Sideband Amplitude Modulation
QoS	Quality of Service

R

R-Profile	Relay Profile
R/W	Read/Write
RACE	Research into Advanced Communications for Europe
RARE	Reseaux Associés pour la Récherche Européenne
RBE	Remote Batch Entry
RBT	Remote Batch Terminal
RD	Request Disconnect (HDLC)
RDA	Receive Data and Acknowledge
RDA	Remote Database Access
RDN	Relative Distinguished Name
RDR	Request Data and Respond
REGIS	Remote Graphics Instruction Set
REJ	Reject

RF	Radio Frequency
RFC	Request for Comments (ARPANET)
RFC	Request for Connection (ARPANET)
RICHE	Réseau d'Information et de Communication Hospitalier Européen
RIU	Ring Interface Unit
RJE	Remote Job Entry
RJEP	Remote Job Entry Protocol
RLF	Reverse Line Feed
RNR	Receive Not Ready
RO	Receive Only
RO	Remote Operations
ROPM	Remote Operations Protocol Machine
ROS	Remote Operations Service
ROSE	Research Open Systems for Europe
ROSE	Remote Operations Service Element
RPC	Remote Procedure Call
RPOA	Recognized Private Operating Agency
RR	Receive Ready
RRE	Royal Radar Establishment
RRJE	Range Remote Job Entry
RS	Record Separator
RS	Recommended Standard (EIA)
RSA	Remote Session Access
RSA	Rivest-Shamir-Adleman
RSEXEC	Resource Sharing Executive
RSRE	Royal Signals and Radar Establishment
RT	Resynchronization Timer
RT	Reliable Transfer
RTOS	Real Time Operating System
RTP	Real Time Protocol
RTS	Request to Send
RTS	Reliable Transfer Server
RTSE	Reliable Transfer Service Element
RTT	Regie des Télégraphes et des Téléphones (Belgian PTT)
RU	Request/Response Unit

S

S/N	Signal to Noise ratio
SA	Source Address
SABM	Set Asynchronous Balanced Mode
SABME	Set Asynchronous Balanced Mode Extended
SACF	Single Association Control Function
SAIL	Serial ASCII Instrument Loop
SAO	Single Association Object
SAP	Service Access Point
SAPI	Service Access Point Identifier
SARM	Set Asynchronous Response Mode
SARME	Set Asynchronous Response Mode Extended
SASE	Specific Application Service Element
SATS	Selected Abstract Test Suite
SC	Session Control
SCS	System Conformance Statement
SCSI	Small Computer Systems Interface
SCTR	System Conformance Test Report
SCVF	Single Channel Voice Frequency
SDE	Submission and Delivery Entity (MHS)
SDIF	Standard Document Interchange Format
SDL	Specification and Description Language
SDLC	Synchronous Data Link Control
SDM	Space Division Multiplexing
SFD	Simple Formattable Document
SFM	Secure File Manager
SFS	Secure File Store
SFS	Shared File System
SGDS	Supergroup Distribution Frame
SGFS	Special Group on Functional Standardization (ISO/IEC JTC1)
SGML	Standard Generalised Markup Language
SHF	Super High Frequency
SIG	Special Interest Group
SITA	Societe Internationale de Telecommunications Aeronautiques
SMAE	Systems Management Application Entity
SMAP	Systems Management Application Protocol

SMAP	Systems Management Application Process
SMASE	Systems Management Application Service Element
SME	Society of Manufacturing Engineers
SMF	System Management Facilities
SMFA	Specific Management Functional Area
SMI	Structure of Management Information
SMIP	Specific Management Information Protocol
SMIS	Specific Management Information Service
SMPDU	Service Message Protocol Data Unit
SMTP	Simple Mail Transfer Protocol
SNACP	Subnetwork Access Protocol
SNDCF	Subnetwork Dependent Convergence Function
SNDCP	Subnetwork Dependent Convergence Protocol
SNICP	Subnetwork-Independent Convergence Protocol
SNPA	Subnetwork Point of Attachment
SNRM	Set Normal Response Mode
SNRME	Set Normal Response Mode Extended
SO	Shift Out
SOG(T)	Senior Officials Group - Telecommunications
SOGITS	Senior Officiais Group - Information Technologies Standardization
SOH	Start of Header
SOM	Start of Message
SPAG	Standards Promotion and Application Group
SPDL	Standard Page Description Language
SPDU	Session Protocol Data Unit
SPM	Session Protocol Machine
SQL	Structured Query Language
SREJ	Selective Reject
SS	Session Service
SSAP	Session Service Access Point
SSB-SC	Single Sideband - Suppressed Carrier
SSCP	System Services Control Point
SSDU	Session-Service-Data-Unit
STD	Subscriber Trunk Dialling
STDM	Statistical Time Division Multiplexing
STE	Signalling Terminal Equipment
STR	Single Token Ring
STX	Start of Text
SUB	Substitute
SUT	System Under Test

SVC	Switched Virtual Circuit
SYN	Synchronous Idle

T

T-Profile	Transport Profile
TA	Terminal Adaptor (ISDN)
TAC	Terminal Access Controller
TAG	Technical Advisory Group
TAP	Terminal Access Point
TAP(C)	Telecommunications Attachments Policy Committee
TASI	Time Assignment Speech Interpolation
TBC	Token Bus Controller
TC	Transmission Control
TC	Technical Corrigendum
TCM	Time Compression Multiplexing
TCP	Transmission Control Program
TCP/IP	Transmission Control Program/Internet Protocol
TDM	Time Division Multiplexing
TDMA	Time Division Multiple Access
TDR	Time Domain Reflectometer
TE	Terminal Equipment (ISDN)
TE	Telecomm Eirann
TED	Trunk Encryption Device
TEDIS	Trade Data Interchange Systems
TELNET	Telecommunication Network
TEMA	Telecommunications Engineering and Manufacturers' Association
TFTP	Trivial File Transfer Protocol
TGM	Trunk Group Multiplexor
THz	Terahertz
TIF	Text Interchange Format
TIP	Terminal Interface Message Processor (ARPANET)
TIU	Trustworthy Interface Unit
TL	Transmission Level

TLP   Transmission Level Point
TMP   Test Management Protocol
TMS   Telephone Management System
TNIU   Trustworthy Network Interface Unit
TOP   Technical and Office Protocols
TP   Transaction Processing
TP-ASE   Transaction Processing Application Service Element
TP-n   Transport Protocol Class n
TPDU   Transport Protocol Data Unit
TPI   Text Preparation and Interchange
TPSE   Transaction Processing Service Element
TPSU   Transaction Processing Service User
TR   Technical Report (ISO)
TRAC   Technical Recommendations Applications Committee
TSAP   Transport Service Access Point
TSDU   Transport Service Data Unit
TSS&TP   Test Suite Structure and Test Purposes
TTCN   Tree and Tabular Combined Notation
TTIU   Trustworthy Terminal Interface Unit
TTXAU   Teletex Access Unit
TTY   Teletypewriter
TUP   Telephone User Parts (ISDN)
TWA   Two Way Alternate
TWS   Two Way Simultaneous
ToD   Time of Day

U

UA   Unnumbered Acknowledgement
UA   User Agent (MHS)
UAE   User Agent Entity
UAL   User Agent Layer
UAPDU   User Agent Protocol Data Unit
UASL   User Agent Sublayer
UCS   Universal Character Set

UDP	Uniform Datagram Protocol
UDPPDU	Unit Data Presentation-protocol-data-unit
UE	User Element
UHF	Ultra High Frequency
UI	Unnumbered Information
UISF	UK ISDN Standards Forum
ULA	Upper Layer Architecture
ULP	Upper Layer Protocol
UMPDU	User Message Protocol Data Unit
US	Unit Separator
UT	Universal Time
UUCP	Unix-to-Unix Call Procedure
UUCP	Unix-to-Unix Copy Program

V

VADS	Value Added Data Service
VAN	Value Added Network
VANS	Value Added Network Service
VC	Virtual Circuit
VDI	Virtual Device Interface
VDL	Vienna Definition Language
VF	Voice Frequency
VFCG	Voice Frequency Telegraph
VFCT	Voice Frequency Carrier Telegraph
VFS	Virtual File Server
VFS	Virtual File Store
VHF	Very High Frequency
VMD	Virtual Manufacturing Device
VRC	Vertical Redundancy Check
VS	Virtual Storage
VSAM	Virtual Sequential Access Method
VSAM	Virtual Storage Access Method
VSB	Vestigial Sideband
VT	Virtual Terminal

VTE-Profile   Virtual Terminal Environment Profile
VTP   Virtual Terminal Protocol

W

WAN   Wide Area Network
WARC   World Administrative Radio Conference
WATS   Wide Area Telephone Service
WATTC   World Administrative Telephone and Telegraph
            Conference
WD   Working Draft
WDM   Wavelength Division Multiplexing
WIMP   Windows, Icons, Mice and Pointers
WMO   World Meteorological Organization
WRU   Who are you (character)

X

X-OFF   Transmitter Off
X-ON   Transmitter On
XBM   Extended Basic Mode
XID   eXchange Identification
XMT   Transmit
XOR   Exclusive OR

0-9

3PMM   3-Phase Modulation Modified

INDEX

A book such as this does not lend itself easily to the production of an index. However, it is helpful to classify the standards listed in the remainder of the book by the relevant OSI layer and that is what this "index" sets out to achieve. Because of the replication of standards by various standards bodies, this "index" only lists ISO standards and CCITT Recommendations (and the latter only where there is no corresponding ISO standard). Within each sub-section, the standards are listed in numerical order of ISO standards then CCITT Recommendations. A brief title is listed but the main part of this book should be consulted for the full title and also the current status (i.e. CD, DIS or full IS).

LAYER INDEPENDENT STANDARDS

Reference Model

ISO 7498	Reference Model
TR 8509	Service conventions
TR 10730	Tutorial on naming and addressing
ISO 10731	Conventions for the definition of OSI services

International Standardized Profiles

TR 10000	ISP taxonomy
ISP 10607	AFTnn - File Transfer, Access and Management
ISP 10608	TAnnn - CO Transport Service over CLNS
ISP 10609	TB, TC, TD and TE - CO Transport Service over CONS

Formal Description Techniques

ISO 8807	LOTOS

ISO 9074	Estelle
TR 9571	LOTOS description of Session Service
TR 9572	LOTOS description of Session Protocol
TR 10023	Formal description of CO Transport Service
TR 10024	Formal description of CO Transport Protocol
TR 10167	Guidelines for the application of Estelle, LOTOS and SDL

Conformance Testing

ISO 9646	Conformance testing methodology
ISO 10025	Conformance testing for CO Transport Protocol over CO Network Service
ISO 10070	Upper Layer Conformance Testing
ISO 10168	Conformance test suite for the Session Protocol
ISO 10169	Conformance test suite for the ACSE Protocol
ISO 10170	Conformance test suite for the FTAM Protocol
TR 10174	LLC-2 test purposes
TR 10183	ODA and ODIF - implementation testing methodology
ISO 10729	Conformance test suite for the Presentation Layer
ISO 10739	Conformance test suite for VT basic class protocol

OSI Management

| ISO 7498-4 | Management framework |

ISO 9595	Management Information Service
ISO 9596	Management Information Protocol
ISO 10040	Systems management overview
ISO 10164	Systems management
ISO 10165	Structure of management information
ISO 10184	Terminal management - model
ISO 10736	Elements of management information related to Transport Layer standards
ISO 10737	Transport Layer management

Security

ISO 7498-2	Security architecture
ISO 8227	DEA1 algorithm
ISO 8372	64-bit block cipher
ISO 8731	Message authentication algorithms
ISO 8732	Key management for message authentication
ISO 9307	DEA2 algorithm
ISO 9788	Peer entity authentication mechanisms
ISO 9796	Digital signature scheme
ISO 9797	Data integrity mechanism
ISO 9798	Peer entity authentication using secret key
ISO 9799	Peer entity authentication using public key
ISO 9979	Registration of cryptographic algorithms
ISO 10116	An n-bit block cipher algorithm
ISO 10117	Peer entity authentication using public key with three-way handshake
ISO 10118	Hash functions for digital signatures

| ISO 10181 | Security frameworks for open systems |

Directories and Registration Authorities

ISO 8859	Registration of graphics character subrepertoires - 8-bit single byte coded graphic character sets
ISO 9594	The Directory
ISO 9834	OSI Registration authorities
TR 9973	Procedures for registration of graphical items

Open Distributed Processing

ISO 9579	Remote database access
ISO 10026	Distributed transaction processing
ISO 10031	Distributed-office-applications Model
ISO 10032	Reference model of data management

Information Resource Dictionary System

| ISO 10027 | IRDS framework |
| ISO 10728 | IRDS Services Interface |

PHYSICAL LAYER

ISO 2110	25-pin connector
ISO 2593	34-pin connector
ISO 4902	37-pin connector
ISO 4903	15-pin connector
ISO 6950	Point-to-point full duplex interface

TR 7477	DTE-DTE connection using V.24 and X.24 circuits
ISO 7480	Start-stop signal quality at the DTE-DCE interface
ISO 8480	DTE/DCE back-up control operation
ISO 8481	DTE-DTE physical connection using X.24 circuits
ISO 8482	Twisted pair multipoint connection
ISO 8867	Industrial asynchronous data link and physical layer
ISO 8877	ISDN basic access connector
ISO 9160	Physical layer interoperability requirements
ISO 9543	Synchronous transmission signal quality at DTE/DCE interfaces
ISO 9549	Galvanic isolation of balanced interchange circuits
ISO 10022	Physical Service definition
ISO 10173	ISDN primary access connector at reference points S and T
I.430	ISDN user-network interface - basic rate
I.431	ISDN user-network interface - primary rate
V.24	DTE/DCE interchange circuits
V.28	Electrical characteristics for unbalanced double-current interchange circuits
V.110/I.463	Support of DTEs with V-series interfaces by an ISDN
X.21	DTE/DCE interface for synchronous operation
X.21*bis*	Use of V-series compatible DTEs on PDNs
X.26	Electrical characteristics for unbalanced double-current interchange circuits

ISO 8471	HDLC - Frame level address assignment
ISO 8885	XID information field content and format
ISO 8886	Data Link service definition
TR 10171	List of data link protocols that use HDLC classes of procedures
I.440/Q.920	ISDN user-network interface - data link layer protocol
I.441/Q.921	ISDN user-network interface - data link layer specification
T.71	LAP-B extended for half-duplex physical link

NETWORK LAYER

ISO 8208	X.25 PLP
ISO 8348	CO Network Service
ISO 8348 AD1	CL Network Service
ISO 8348 AD2	Network Layer addressing
ISO 8472	X.25(1980) network convergence protocol
ISO 8648	Internal organisation of the Network Layer
ISO 8743	CL Network Service protocol
ISO 8878	Use of X.25 for CONS
ISO 8880	Network Service over a LAN
ISO 8881	Use of X.25 PLP over LANs
ISO 8882	X.25-DTE conformance testing
ISO 9068	CL Network Service
ISO 9542	Routing protocol for CLNS
ISO 9574	CONS using ISDN
TR 9575	Routing framework
TR 9577	Protocol identification

TRANSPORT LAYER

SESSION LAYER

ISO 8326	Session Service definition
ISO 8327	CO Session Protocol specification
ISO 9548	CL Session protocol
ISO 10168	Conformance test suite for the Session Protocol

PRESENTATION LAYER

ISO 8822	CO Presentation Service definition
ISO 8822 AD1	CL Presentation Service definition
ISO 8823	CO Presentation Protocol specification
ISO 8824	ASN.1
ISO 8825	ASN.1 Encoding Rules
ISO 9576	Presentation CL protocol to provide CL Presentation Services
ISO 10729	Conformance test suite for the Presentation Layer

APPLICATION LAYER

ISO 9545	Application Layer Structure

Service Elements

ISO 8649	Association Control Service Element
ISO 10169	Conformance test suite for the ACSE Protocol
ISO 8650	Association Control Protocol
ISO 10035	Connectionless ACSE protocol specification

ISO 9066	Reliable transfer
ISO 9072	Remote operations
ISO 9804	CCR Service Element
ISO 9805	CCR Protocol
ISO 10148	RPC using OSI Remote Operations

Specific Service Elements

ISO 8571	FTAM
ISO 10170	Conformance test suite for the FTAM Protocol
ISO 8831	JTM Concepts and Services
ISO 8832	JTM protocol
ISO 9040	VT services
ISO 9041	VT protocol
ISO 10739	Conformance test suite for VT basic class protocol
ISO 9506	MMS
TR 7352	Guidelines for representation of data elements
ISO 7372	Trade data elements directory
ISO 9735	EDIFACT
TR 9789	Guidelines for representation of data elements - coding methods and principles
ISO 9955	Application protocols for banking information interchange
ISO 10021	Message Oriented Text Interchange System
X.400	Message handling systems
ISO 10160	Interlibrary loan application service definition

ISO 10161	Interlibrary loan application protocol specification
ISO 10162	Bibliographic search, retrieve and update service definition
ISO 10163	Bibliographic search, retrieve and update protocol specification

LOCAL AREA NETWORKS

ISO 8802-2	Logical link control
ISO 8802-3	CSMA/CD
ISO 8802-4	Token bus
ISO 8802-5	Token ring
ISO 8802-7	Slotted ring
ISO 9314	FDDI
TR 9578	Interface connectors
ISO 10038	MAC bridging
ISO 10039	MAC service definition
TR 10174	LLC-2 test purposes
TR 10178	Structure and coding of LSAP addresses
TR 10734	Guidelines for bridged LAN source routing operation by end systems
TR 10735	MAC addresses
DIS 25014	CSMA/CD 10 Mbit/s baseband planning and installation guide

COMPUTER GRAPHICS

| ISO 7942 | GKS functional description |
| ISO 8632 | Metafile for picture description information |

ISO 8651	GKS language bindings
ISO 8805	GKS-3D functional description
ISO 8806	GKS-3D language bindings
ISO 9592	PHIGS functional description
ISO 9593	PHIGS language bindings
ISO 9636	CGI
ISO 9637	CGI data encoding
ISO 9638	CGI language bindings

DATABASES

ISO 8907	NDL
ISO 9075	SQL
ISO 9579	Remote database access

OFFICE SYSTEMS

ISO 8613	ODA/ODIF
TR 10183	ODA and ODIF - implementation testing methodology
ISO 8879	SGML
ISO 9069	SGML document interchange format
ISO 9070	SGML support facilities
ISO 9541	Font and character information interchange
TR 9573	Techniques for using SGML
TR 10037	Guidelines for SGML syntax-directed editing systems
ISO 10166	Document filing and retrieval (DFR)
ISO 10175	Document printing application

| ISO 10179 | DSSSL - Document style semantics and specification language |
| ISO 10180 | Standard Page Description Language |

CHARACTER CODING

ISO 646	ISO 7-bit code
ISO 963	Derivation of 4-bit codes
ISO 2022	7-bit and 8-bit codes - code extension techniques
ISO 2375	Registration of escape sequences
ISO 2047	Graphical representation of control characters
ISO 4873	ISO 8-bit code
ISO 6429	7-bit and 8-bit codes - additional control functions
ISO 6936	Conversion between ISO 7-bit code and IA2
ISO 6937	Coded character sets for text communication
ISO 8884	Keyboards for multiple latin alphabets
ISO 9541	Font and character information interchange
ISO 10367	8-bit code for information interchange
ISO 10538	Control functions for text communication
ISO 10646	Universal coded character set
S.1	ITA No 2
S.18	Conversion between ITA No 2 and IA5
T.50	IA5